FABLES: MARCH OF THE WOODEN SOLDIERS

FABLES CREATED BY BILL WILLINGHAM

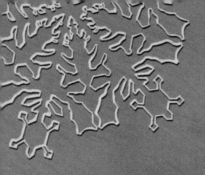

KAREN BERGER
VP-Executive Editor

SHELLY BOND
Editor-original series

MARIAH HUEHNER
Assistant Editor-original series

SCOTT NYBAKKEN
Editor-collected edition

ROBBIN BROSTERMAN
Senior Art Director

PAUL LEVITZ
President & Publisher

GEORG BREWER
VP-Design & Retail Product Development

RICHARD BRUNING
Senior VP-Creative Director

PATRICK CALDON
Senior VP-Finance & Operations

CHRIS CARAMALIS
VP-Finance

TERRI CUNNINGHAM
VP-Managing Editor

DAN DIDIO
VP-Editorial

ALISON GILL
VP-Manufacturing

RICH JOHNSON
VP-Book Trade Sales

HANK KANALZ
VP-General Manager, WildStorm

LILLIAN LASERSON
Senior VP & General Counsel

JIM LEE
Editorial Director-WildStorm

DAVID MCKILLIPS
VP-Advertising & Custom Publishing

JOHN NEE
VP-Business Development

GREGORY NOVECK
Senior VP-Creative Affairs

CHERYL RUBIN
Senior VP-Brand Management

BOB WAYNE
VP-Sales & Marketing

FABLES: MARCH OF THE WOODEN SOLDIERS

Published by DC Comics. Cover, compilation and
Who's who in Fabletown copyright © 2004
DC Comics. All Rights Reserved.

Originally published in single magazine form as
FABLES: THE LAST CASTLE and FABLES 19-21,
23-27. Copyright © 2003, 2004 Bill Willingham
and DC Comics. All Rights Reserved.
All characters, their distinctive likenesses and
related elements featured in this publication
are trademarks of Bill Willingham. VERTIGO is
a trademark of DC Comics. The stories, characters
and incidents featured in this publication are
entirely fictional. DC Comics does not read or
accept unsolicited submissions of ideas, stories
or artwork.

DC Comics, 1700 Broadway, New York, NY 10019
A Warner Bros. Entertainment Company.
Printed in Canada. First Printing.
ISBN: 1-4012-0222-5

Cover illustration by James Jean.

*This war story is for my MP Army
buddies, Bill Heck, Mike Lyons and
Joe Czuchra, partners in crime, and
fighting, and in crime-fighting. Veterans
of the Cold War, they stood their posts on
our side of the wall, ten years before the
wall came down.*

— Bill Willingham

*This book is dedicated to Mum, Dad,
Claire, Jason and Rudy... for love and
support always. It's also for Irma, my
true love and inspiration. And finally, it's
dedicated to the memory of William and
Amy Breddy, my grandparents, in whose
home I drew every page of this volume.*

— Mark Buckingham

Table of Contents

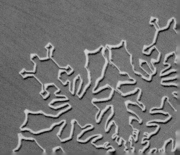

WHO'S WHO IN FABLETOWN

ROSE RED

Former wild child and Snow White's occasionally estranged twin sister. She runs the Farm now — the upstate Fabletown annex where all of the nonhuman-looking Fables are forced to live.

SNOW WHITE

She's Fabletown's no-nonsense deputy mayor and the one who holds it all together. Briefly married to the philandering Prince Charming before the exile, she recently discovered that she has become pregnant with Bigby Wolf's child, when they were both under an evil enchantment.

PRINCE CHARMING

He's the perennial rogue — silver-tongued, dashing, cultured and far too pretty for a man. Formerly wed to Snow White, Sleeping Beauty and Cinderella, in that order, he lost each of them shortly after the wooing ended and the actual hard work of marriage began. Recently he killed Bluebeard in a duel and started a campaign to become the next mayor of Fabletown.

CLARA

Formerly a fire-breathing dragon, now she's a fire-breathing raven. She's Rose Red's personal bodyguard and enforcer, and the chief reason no one at the Farm is likely to rebel ever again.

BOY BLUE

Snow White's efficient and able assistant, and a steadfast player of the blues.

BIGBY WOLF

Big and bad when he wants to be, and a real wolf when he needs to be, he's the sheriff of Fabletown. Reformed, reliable and trustworthy, he's recently admitted to carrying a longtime torch for Snow White.

JACK HORNER

A would-be trickster and lifelong con artist, he's the Jack of both beanstalk and giant-killer fame and star of most of the other Jack Tales. He was briefly romantically involved with Rose Red, his partner in one of his many failed get-rich schemes.

BEAUTY AND THE BEAST

Poor but eternally ambitious, they're Fabletown's most stable married couple. Unfortunately the old enchantment is still active and he turns back into a beast exactly to the extent that she is mad at him at any given time.

PINOCCHIO

Carved by cranky old Gepetto from the wood of a magic grove, he's now a real boy, but one who can never grow up, because the Blue Fairy took his wish to become a real boy just a bit too literally.

KING COLE

The affable, glad-handing mayor of Fabletown since its founding centuries ago. For the first time his re-election isn't just a *pro forma* event. Now he's facing Prince Charming in a real election.

THE THREE BEARS

Mama, Papa and Baby (Boo) Bear. They were caught taking part in the recent rebellion attempt at the Farm and were sentenced to many years of hard labor for their crimes.

WEYLAND SMITH

He can build anything and he's a good man to have at your back when the chips are down. He lives at the Farm, converting modern weapons into versions usable by intelligent animals, in preparation for that day when they all march back to retake their lost homelands from the Adversary and his legions.

HOBBES

Formerly Bluebeard's goblin butler, now he's switched his loyalties to Prince Charming.

FLYCATCHER

The Frog Prince of old, who can't quite get over his taste for flies. These minor infractions keep him endlessly piled up with hours upon hours of community service punishment details, which never seem to end.

MUSTARD POT PETE

A socially gregarious bug who lives at the Farm in his cozy mustard pot and watches the Farm's office during the night shift.

GRIMBLE

The under-the-bridge troll of Billy Goats Gruff fame. Now, in human guise, he's the usually-sleeping but ever-watchful security guard at the Woodland Building — Fabletown's unofficial city hall.

THE STORY SO FAR

For many centuries, refugee Fables have been living among us in a secret New York City community they call Fabletown. They were driven from their original magic homelands, which fell to the conquering armies of a feared being known only as the Adversary. (Some of their adventures since arriving here have already been chronicled in the previous Fables volumes: LEGENDS IN EXILE, ANIMAL FARM and STORYBOOK LOVE.) For all of these long years the exiled Fables lived in relative peace, gradually growing convinced that the Adversary had no further interest in them or their adopted mundane world. No new Fable refugees have arrived in Fabletown or the New World for more than a century...

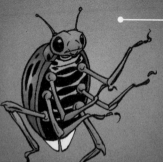

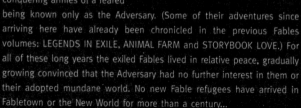

BUT NO, MISS WHITE, I DON'T HAVE A CLUB TRYOUT.

THEN WHAT'S GOT YOU IN SUCH A MELANCHOLY MOOD TODAY?

IT'S THE IDES OF MAY.

OH.

I FORGOT.

I SHOULD HAVE MENTIONED IT. I'M SORRY I'M NOT GETTING ANYTHING DONE. I'LL COME IN EARLY TOMORROW AND WORK *TWICE* AS HARD TO MAKE UP FOR IT.

NO, YOU WON'T. IF LAST YEAR, AND EVERY YEAR *BEFORE* THAT, IS ANY INDICATION, YOU'LL BE TOO *HUNG OVER* TO COME IN AT ALL.

GUILTY AS CHARGED. I NEVER *PLAN* TO DRINK AS MUCH AS I DO, BUT IT ALWAYS ENDS UP EASIER THAN FACING THE NIGHT SOBER.

I GUESS YOU'D HAVE TO *BE* THERE TO UNDERSTAND.

EXCEPT THAT I'M NEVER INVITED.

I UNDER-
STAND,
THOUGH.

THIS MINI REMEMBRANCE DAY IS
STRICTLY RESERVED FOR THOSE OF YOU
ON THE LAST BOAT OUT.

SUPER
SECRET. **MOST**
PRIVATE.

NO ONE WHO
WASN'T THERE IS
WELCOME.

IT'S NOT
LIKE THAT.

IT'S NO
BIG **SECRET**,
EXCEPT THAT--

--I'M NOT
SURE HOW TO
DESCRIBE IT.

WE **HAVE** TO DO THIS
EVERY YEAR. IT'S A DUTY, NOT
A CELEBRATION. INVITING OTHERS
WOULD FEEL LIKE TRYING TO
SHIFT THE BURDEN ONTO
SOMEONE ELSE.

AH, **I**
GET IT. YOU
DON'T WANT TO
DILUTE THE
GUILT BY
SHARING
IT.

SOME-
THING LIKE
THAT I
GUESS.

I'M NOT
EXPLAINING
IT VERY
WELL.

BUT I'D TELL YOU,
MISS WHITE, IF
YOU WANTED TO
KNOW WHAT **HAP-
PENED** BACK THEN.

THEN I'M
ALL EARS.
LORD KNOWS
WE'RE NOT
GOING TO GET
ANYTHING
ELSE DONE
TODAY.

TELL ME YOUR TALE, BOY BLUE.

"OKAY, WHAT WAS IT--THE EARLY NINETEENTH CENTURY HERE? YOU'D BEEN IN THE MUNDY WORLD FOR SEVERAL CENTURIES BY THEN, AND FABLETOWN WAS WELL ESTABLISHED.

"NAPOLEON'S ARMIES WERE SWEEPING ACROSS EUROPE AT THE TIME, WHICH I *STILL* THINK WAS CAUSED BY SOME FORM OF SYMPATHETIC MAGIC--MAYBE NOT INTENTIONALLY--BUT IT REFLECTED WHAT THE ADVERSARY'S LEGIONS WERE DOING TO OUR HOMELANDS.

"BY THEN, MOST OF US WHO WERE GOING TO ESCAPE ALREADY HAD.

"THE ADVERSARY HAD CONQUERED EVERYTHING. NO KINGDOM COULD WITHSTAND HIM. NO ARMY SURVIVED INTACT TO TAKE THE FIELD AGAINST HIM.

SHE MIGHT ACTUALLY MAKE IT, BROTHER EFRAM.

NOT IF SHE'S MET BY A LOCKED *DOOR* AT THE END OF HER RIDE, BROTHER JOEL. FLY AHEAD AND TELL THEM TO OPEN THE GATE.

"EVERY MAGIC DOORWAY FROM THE HOMELANDS TO THE NEW WORLD HAD BEEN LOCATED, BLOCKED OR *DESTROYED* BY THEN ...

"...EXCEPT ONE."

The Last Castle

"THE FAR KEEP AT THE END OF THE KNOWN WORLDS—EAST OF THE SUN AND WEST OF THE MOON—WAS WHERE ONE LAST GATEWAY TO FREEDOM STILL EXISTED. IT WAS GUARDED BY THE CRUMBLING, BATTERED WALLS OF THE FORTRESS AND THE LAST HANDFUL OF FREE DEFENDERS LEFT TO MAN THEM."

SIX GOOD TARGETS COMING INTO RANGE.

SO FEW?

HARDLY WORTH STRINGING MY **BOW**.

"THE ADVERSARY'S LEGIONS HAD FOUND THEIR WAY TO US-- *FINALLY*, ONE SUPPOSES, RUNNING OUT OF ANYONE OR ANYTHING ELSE TO DESTROY.

IF YOU'RE NOT ALREADY TOO DRUNK TO *SEE* STRAIGHT, OLD TUCK.

"THEIR SKIRMISHERS HAD FILLED THE VALLEY FOR DAYS IN ADVANCE OF THE MAIN ARMY.

"THEY'D QUICKLY CUT OFF OUR SUPPLY LINES AND ANY HOPE OF FURTHER REINFORCEMENTS.

OPEN THE *GATE*, YOU BLIND *BASTARDS!*

CAN'T YOU SEE A *RIDER'S* COMING?

AHH!

THUNK

"AND OF COURSE THEY *INTERCEPTED* ANY LATE REFUGEES TRYING TO MAKE IT TO THE LAST REMAINING FOOTHOLD OF FREEDOM IN A HUNDRED CONQUERED LANDS.

"IN THE PAST WEEK THE FLOW OF REFUGEES HAD BEEN CUT DOWN TO A TRICKLE--

"--BARELY ONE IN *FIVE* REACHED OUR WALLS ALIVE."

"AND NONE AT ALL IN THE LAST TWO DAYS.

HELP ME!

--ARRUP--

"UNTIL *SHE* SHOWED UP, ALL ALONE, OUT OF THE BLUE.

"SHE WAS THE LAST TO REACH US...

"...ALIVE IN ONLY THE MOST *RUDIMENTARY* SENSE OF THE WORD."

ONE TO ONE SO FAR, MY LADY.

ONE TO *TWO*, LOXLEY, MY SHOT PIERCED HIS EYE.

"BY THEN I WAS IN MY *FIFTEENTH* YEAR FIGHTING THE INVADERS.

BLUE BOY?

DAMN IT ALL, WHERE'S MY *ORDERLY?*

"I SERVED IN COLONEL BEARSKIN'S FREE COMPANY. I WAS WITH HIM IN ALL THE FAMOUS BATTLES YOU'VE HEARD ABOUT, OVER AND AGAIN.

HERE, SIR! *SORRY,* SIR! THERE WAS A LINE AT THE GUARDROBE.

GET DOWN TO THE INFIRMARY. IF THAT RIDER *LIVES,* I WANT YOU THERE WHEN HE *WAKES.*

"BOXEN, RUBY LAKE, OAKCOURT, AND THE HELLISH ROUT AT HOLLYFIELD, WHERE THEY CUT US DOWN BY THE *THOUSANDS,* LEAVING US WITH LESS THAN A THIRD OF THE MEN WE ARRIVED WITH THAT MORNING.

WHAT RIDER, SIR? I DIDN'T SEE--

I COULDN'T *SWEAR* TO IT BUT I THINK "HE" WAS A SHE, ACTUALLY.

"THAT USHERED IN NEARLY A YEAR OF CONSTANT RETREAT, AS THE COLONEL CUNNINGLY MANEUVERED TO SAVE WHAT REMAINED OF HIS ARMY.

I'LL WANT ANY NEW INTELLIGENCE SHE CAN PROVIDE ON ENEMY STRENGTH AND POSITION.

RIGHT AWAY, SIR.

"WE FLED BEYOND THE HOUSES OF THE FOUR WINDS, NO LONGER CLINGING TO ANY HOPE THAT WE COULD WIN AGAINST THE ADVERSARY."

WHAT DID YOU AND YOUR BROTHERS SPY, SQUIRE VULCO?

IT'S THEIR MAIN ARMY, UNDER GENERAL DE BEAUCAIRE, AS WE FEARED, SIR. THEY'RE A DAY AWAY, AT *MOST.*

"EVENTUALLY WE FOUND OUR WAY TO THE FAR KEEP, WHERE WE FINALLY TURNED TO MAKE OUR LAST STAND IN THE HOME-LANDS--TO PROTECT, AS LONG AS POSSIBLE, THE ONLY REMAINING GATE-WAY TO THE MUNDY WORLD.

"IN ONES OR TWOS, OR SMALL HANDFULS, OTHERS RALLIED TO OUR BANNER--PEASANTS AND NOBLES AND FIGURES I'D EVER ONLY HEARD OF IN WHISPERED LEGENDS.

"THE NOTORIOUS OUTLAW ROBIN O' THE WOODS LED HIS FAMOUS MIRY MEN TO STAND WITH US.

I'LL HELP YOU FIND THE **BEST** DRESS HERE, ROB. NO **LADY** WILL REFUSE THE SOLEMN REQUEST OF CLERGY.

YOU'LL BE THE **BELLE** OF THE **BALL**, I'LL WARRANT.

"THE KING OF MADAGAO ARRIVED, WITH HIS SURVIVING KNIGHTS AND MEN AT ARMS.

WHAT ARE THE **BORNEGASCARIANS** DOING HERE? YOU'D THINK THEY'D BE **HAPPIER** ALLIED WITH THE ADVERSARY.

"MADAGAO'S LONG-TIME ENEMY, THE KING OF BORNE-GASCAR, ARRIVED AT THE HEAD OF HIS REMAINING FORCES, PUTTING ASIDE OLD ENMITIES TO ALLY AGAINST THE GREATER THREAT."

FILTHY MADAGOANS. NOTE, GENTLEMEN, HOW QUICKLY THEY **SURRENDER** WHEN THE FIGHTING STARTS!

"GREAT OLD PELLINORE INTERRUPTED HIS ENDLESS QUEST TO JOIN US.

"THE REDCROSS KNIGHT.

"SIR HERMAN VON STARKENFAUST, WHO TURNED OUT NOT TO BE A GHOST AFTER ALL.

GOOD PARRY, MEIN HERR.

"TAM LIN, THE KNIGHT LOVED BY THE QUEEN OF FAIRY HERSELF.

"EACH MORE EXTRAORDINARY THAN THE LAST.

PUT THAT MEAT CLEAVER *AWAY*, BUTCHER BOY. I'M A SPECIAL KIND OF COW. THE ONLY LIVING MEMBER OF SPECIES BOVALUNARIS. YOU DON'T MAKE *STEAKS* OUT OF SOMEONE WHO'S BEEN TO THE *MOON* AND BACK.

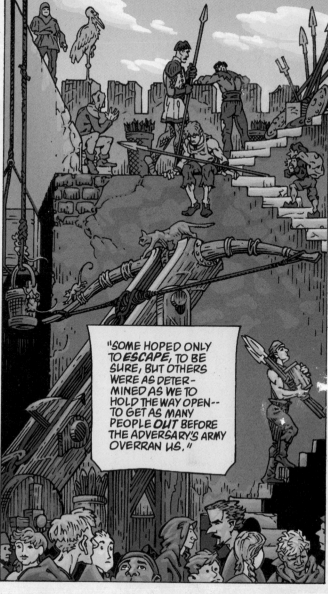

"SOME HOPED ONLY TO *ESCAPE*, TO BE SURE, BUT OTHERS WERE AS DETERMINED AS WE TO HOLD THE WAY OPEN -- TO GET AS MANY PEOPLE *OUT* BEFORE THE ADVERSARY'S ARMY OVERRAN US."

"WE WERE ALL WAITING FOR OUR SHIP TO COME IN.

HEAVE!

HAVE YOUR MEN PUT THEIR *BACKS* INTO IT, CAPTAIN. TIME IS MONEY.

YES, Y'GRACE.

HEAVE, YOU LUBBERS!

IT'S *HERE!*

PASS THE WORD UP TO THE COLONEL! THE SHIP IS *HERE!*

FULL MOON TO-NIGHT.

IS THAT A GOOD OMEN, OR BAD?

I IMAGINE WE'VE USED UP ALL OF OUR *GOOD* OMENS FOR THIS LIFE-TIME.

OOOOHHHNNNN

WELCOME TO THE KEEP AT THE END OF THE WORLD.

I'M-- YOU CAN CALL ME *BLUE*.

I'M AIDE DE CAMP TO COLONEL BEARSKIN, COMMANDER OF THE LAST OF ALL FREE COMPANIES.

WHO... WHAT *HAPPENED* TO ME?

"I PASSED THAT EVENING WATCHING HER SLEEP. I DON'T KNOW WHAT OCCURRED IN THE REST OF THE KEEP.

WHY IS THAT *MAN* IN A *DRESS?*

I *ASSURE* YOU, LORD BLUEBEARD, I HAVE *NARY* AN IDEA.

THIS *RATHOLE* TURNS MORE CHAOTIC EVERY TRIP I *MAKE.*

WHERE'S YOUR COLONEL BEARSHIRT TONIGHT?

THAT WOULD BE *BEARSKIN,* SIR. HE TAKES HIS MEALS IN HIS QUARTERS, AND LACKING AN *EMERGENCY,* WON'T BE DISTURBED UNTIL MORNING.

NONSENSE. I WANT TO GET MY SHIP LOADED AND OUT OF HERE AT FIRST LIGHT.

NOT WITHOUT HIS LEAVE, SIR.

THEN MAKE SURE I'M FIRST ON HIS RECEIVING LIST IN THE *MORNING.*

YOU'RE THE PRINCE OF *CHARMERS.* WHY CAN'T YOU GET US BETTER *LODGINGS?*

THIS IS AN *ESCAPE,* NOT A WEEKEND IN THE COUNTRY, CINDER DEAR. AND THEY'RE CALLED *QUARTERS* ON A MILITARY POST.

AND DIDN'T I GET US *THIS* FAR WITH OUR SKINS INTACT? THAT'S *SOMETHING,* MY TURTLEDOVE.

WHAT WILL THIS MUNDY WORLD BE LIKE? IS IT TRUE THAT *BOTH* OF YOUR PREVIOUS WIVES ARE THERE ALREADY?

GOD, I *HOPE* NOT. IT'S SUPPOSED TO BE A *REFUGE* AFTER ALL.

THE NEXT DAY WASN'T SO ENJOYABLE.

THAT MORNING, THE ADVERSARY'S ARMY SHOWED UP.

AND CONTINUED SHOWING UP THROUGHOUT THE DAY.

UNTIL, BY THAT EVENING, THEY FILLED THE LENGTH AND BREADTH OF OUR CORNER OF THE WORLD.

"I'M NOT SURE HOW LONG IT LASTED-- PROBABLY ONLY MINUTES, IN RETROSPECT.

"BY THE TIME THEY'D BROKEN AND RUN, WE'D SUFFERED ONLY A FEW WOUNDS AND ONE MORTAL LOSS, COMPARED TO OVER THREE HUNDRED OF THEIR DEAD."

"IT WAS A ROUT, AND WE CELEBRATED IT WITH AN ENTHUSIASM ONLY EXPERIENCED BY VETERAN SOLDIERS WHO'VE REALIZED THEY GET TO *LIVE* A LITTLE WHILE LONGER."

LORD ABOVE. CHOPPING SO MANY RIPE MELONS MAKES FOR *THIRSTY* WORK. SOMEONE BREAK OUT THE *WINE.*

WE *DID* IT, SIR! WE *BEAT* THEM!

DON'T BE *RIDICULOUS,* BOY. THEY DIDN'T USE A *FRACTION* OF THEIR FORCES.

DON'T DOUBT THAT WHEN ALL IS SAID AND DONE, THE *ONLY* ONES OF US LEAVING THIS FORT ALIVE WILL BE THOSE LUCKY FEW ON BLUEBEARD'S SHIP...

...PROVIDED WE CAN HOLD THIS PLACE *LONG* ENOUGH FOR THEM TO GET AWAY.

"THE ENEMY'S NEXT MOVE WAS MORE *SURPRISING.*"

LOOK, SIR!

A WHITE FLAG!

PERHAPS I SPOKE TOO SOON...

...NO DOUBT THEY'VE ONLY JUST *LEARNED* THE FEARED BOY BLUE IS AMONG THE DEFENDERS HERE AND HAVE DECIDED TO SURRENDER TO *YOU.*

I SUPPOSE WE SHOULD GO *TALK* TO THEM, YOU AND I.

"AS HIS ORDERLY I WAS HONORABLY REQUIRED TO ACCOMPANY MY COLONEL OUT TO THE PARLEY, THOUGH I DEARLY WISHED OTHERWISE.

WHAT WILL WE DO IF THIS IS A *TRICK* ?

IN *THAT* CASE OUR PART'S NOT COMPLICATED, SON. WE *DIE.*

AND THEN THE OTHERS WILL NO DOUBT CHOOSE A *NEW* LEADER -- ONE WHO IS *SMART* ENOUGH NOT TO MAKE THE SAME MISTAKE.

"MY STEPS DIDN'T QUITE FALTER, NOR DID MY KNEES QUITE BUCKLE, BUT I LONGED FOR THE RELATIVE SAFETY OF THE KEEP'S HIGH WALLS."

AH, LOOK, IT'S COLONEL BEARSKIN. WHAT AN UNEXPECTED *PLEASURE.* I NEVER *DARED* HOPE IT MIGHT BE YOU I WAS FACING TODAY.

FACING *AGAIN,* YOU MEAN.

YOU WERE IN COMMAND AT BOXEN, WEREN'T YOU? I BEAT YOU THEN, COUNT AUCASSIN DE BEAUCAIRE.

OUT-*MANEUVERED* ME, PERHAPS.

AND NOW YOUR LATEST ATTACK *FAILED.*

THAT WAS HARDLY AN *ATTACK,* DREAD COLONEL, MERELY A SMALL *DEMON-STRATION* TO ESTABLISH FIRST PRINCIPALS --TO SHOW THAT I'M WILLING TO SPEND TROOPS. I'LL *GLADLY* WASTE A THOUSAND OF *THEM* JUST TO GET ONE OF *YOU.*

MY MASTER SUMMONED THESE *GUTTER RACES* UP FROM THE INFERNAL PITS FOR JUST SUCH A *PURPOSE.*

THE COMMON JOKE IS: THEIR OWN NAME FOR THEIR RACE TRANSLATES INTO OUR TONGUE AS...

...Heh...

..."ARCHERY TARGETS."

BUT I'M BEING *RUDE.* I'D INTENDED TO OFFER YOU *REFRESHMENT* BEFORE WE GOT DOWN TO BUSINESS. DO *PLEASE* SIT DOWN.

NO, THANK YOU. I'M *PARTICULAR* ABOUT WHO I DRINK WITH. WHY DON'T YOU JUST SAY WHAT YOU *INTEND* TO SAY?

VERY WELL, THEN. YOU'RE OUT-NUMBERED BY AN *OVERWHELMING* FACTOR. YOU CAN'T WIN AND YOU CAN'T GET AWAY. MY ORDERS ARE TO KILL YOU--*ALL* OF YOU.

--EVEN UNTO THE SMALLEST CHILD.

BUT AT THE RISK OF INCURRING MY MASTER'S *DISPLEASURE*, I'M PREPARED TO OFFER YOU *BETTER* TERMS THAN THAT. IF YOU SURRENDER *NOW*, I'LL SPARE THE WOMEN AND CHILDREN.

THEY'LL LIVE IN DIRE CAPTIVITY...

...BUT AT LEAST THEY'LL *LIVE.*

HOW LONG DO WE HAVE TO DECIDE?

NO TIME AT ALL. CHOOSE *NOW.*

I CAN'T. THIS TIME I'M ONLY *NOMINALLY* IN CHARGE OF A MIXED FORCE. I'LL HAVE TO CONSULT THE OTHER COMMANDERS.

VERY WELL. GO BACK AND *TAKE* YOUR MEETING. DON'T DELAY, THOUGH. YOU HAVE UNTIL I BECOME *BORED* WITH SITTING OUT HERE.

"RETURNING--WITH MY UNPROTECTED *BACK* FACING THE ENEMY--WAS *WORSE.* I SWEAR I COULD FEEL THEIR ARROWS CENTERED ON ME."

YOU'LL *KNOW* THAT THE TIME HAS FINALLY RUN OUT WHEN YOU FEEL MY *SWORD* SLICE THROUGH YOUR OVER-LARGE NECK.

"THAT NIGHT THE COLONEL CALLED US ALL TOGETHER IN THE UPPER WARD."

FRIENDS--DEAR COMRADES IN ARMS--IT SEEMS TIME HAS FINALLY RUN *OUT* FOR US. THIS *BOAT* WILL BE THE *LAST ONE OUT.*

BUT IT WON'T HOLD *ALL* OF US.

EVEN *WERE* IT SO, SOME OF US HAVE TO REMAIN *BEHIND* TO BUY IT ENOUGH TIME TO GET SAFELY *AWAY.*

SINCE IT CAN'T NAVIGATE THE RIVER AT *NIGHT,* IT WILL LEAVE AT FIRST *LIGHT.*

PLACES ON BOARD WILL BE ASSIGNED AS FOLLOWS: FIRST PRIORITY IS GIVEN TO *WOMEN* AND *CHILDREN* OF COURSE, ALONG WITH *NON-HUMAN* FABLES.

THEN, *MARRIED* MEN WHOSE WIVES OR FAMILIES ARE EITHER *ABOARD* ON THIS TRIP OR *ALREADY* IN THE MUNDANE WORLD.

I'M SAVED.

OH, MY COURA- GEOUS PRINCE.

WE'LL HOLD *OUT* AS LONG AS WE CAN, BUT ONCE WE *FALL* HERE, IT WILL BE UP TO *YOU* TO PROTECT THE *SHIP.*

LORD BLUEBEARD, I'LL ALSO PREVAIL ON *YOU* TO TAKE OUT WITH YOU THE MAGIC ARTIFACTS WE STILL HAVE STORED HERE--PRIMARILY ANYTHING THAT COULD *AID* THE EMPEROR OR HIS ARMIES.

OF COURSE.

EXCEPT THE *WITCHING CLOAK.* I'LL HAVE NEED OF THAT HERE.

ONLY THEN, IF *ANY* ROOM REMAINS, ADDITIONAL BERTHS WILL BE FILLED BY *LOTTERY.*

I'M EXCUSING *MYSELF* FROM THAT LOTTERY THOUGH, AND ANYONE ELSE WHO VOLUNTEERS TO REMAIN BEHIND SHOULD SEE *ME* AFTER WE'RE DONE HERE.

NO *NEED* TO SEE YOU IN PRIVATE. I *WON'T* BE GOING.

NOR *ME!*

I'LL STAY!

THE KING OF MADAGAO *WON'T* FLEE WHILE OTHERS STAY IN HIS PLACE.

IF EVEN MADAGAO HAS THE *COURAGE* TO STAY, CAN BORNEGASCAR SHOW LESS FORTITUDE?

"PREPARATIONS GOT UNDER WAY QUICKLY THEN.

I WONDER WHAT THESE BRAVE **WARRIORS** WOULD SAY IF THEY KNEW THE **NOBLE** PRINCE CHARMING PLANS TO **DIVORCE** THE WOMAN HE'S USING TO SAVE HIS **MISERABLE** LIFE.

WILL YOU **KEEP** YOUR **VOICE** DOWN, WOMAN! IF SOMEONE **HEARS**--!

YOU MIGHT HAVE TO STAY BEHIND WITH THE **REAL** MEN? THAT WOULD BE A BLESSING IN **SO** MANY WAYS.

BUT DON'T WORRY. I'LL PLAY THE **LOVING** WIFE LONG ENOUGH TO SECURE YOUR SEAT ON THE RESCUE BOAT.

BUT ONCE IN THIS **FABLETOWN** PLACE, I'LL THANK YOU TO **DIVORCE** ME AND THEN **IMMEDIATELY** LEAVE FOR ANY OTHER COUNTRY IN THAT WORLD.

OH!

HELLO! BOY BLUE!

GREAT TO SUDDENLY SEE YOU, FROM OUT OF **NOWHERE!**

WE WEREN'T **DOING** ANYTHING.

NOTHING WRONG. JUST **TALKING.**

HUSBAND AND **WIFE** STUFF IS ALL.

PRIVATE THINGS.

YOU DIDN'T **HEAR** US... **DID** YOU?

UHM... NO.

AH!

DO YOU KNOW MY **DEARLY** BELOVED WIFE, THE PRINCESS CINDERELLA?

YES, WE'VE MET. THIS IS THE LADY RIDING HOOD.

WELL... THESE ARE **HEAVY** AND WE HAVE TO GET THEM **ABOARD**, SO...

GOOD NIGHT.

WATCH OUT-- THESE STEPS CAN GET **SLIPPERY.**

YOU DON'T HAVE TO MAKE UP **EXCUSES** TO HOLD MY **HAND,** SIR.

IT'S NOT...

I DON'T--

I DIDN'T--

BOY BLUE, SHIRKING YOUR **DUTY** AGAIN, I SEE.

DOESN'T **LOOK** MUCH LIKE SLEEPING TO ME, LAD.

THE COLONEL **INSISTED** I GET A FEW HOURS' SLEEP BEFORE MY NEXT WATCH.

MISS RIDING HOOD, THIS IS VULCO. HE'S ONE OF THE TWELVE CROW BROTHERS.

ONLY **NINE** OF US LEFT NOW. WE'VE SUFFERED SOME ATTRITION AS THE COMPANY'S MAIN SCOUTS. YOU MIGHT HAVE NOTICED US **ESCORT**-ING YOU IN, YESTERDAY-- FLYING OVERHEAD.

FLYING? BUT--?

PLEASED AS FRESH **BUGS** TO MEET YOU, LASS, BUT AS I SUSPECT YOU TWO MIGHT BE AFTER SOME **PRIVACY** UP HERE. I'LL DEFTLY EXCUSE MYSELF NOW.

UHM... THANK YOU.

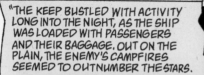

"THE KEEP BUSTLED WITH ACTIVITY LONG INTO THE NIGHT, AS THE SHIP WAS LOADED WITH PASSENGERS AND THEIR BAGGAGE. OUT ON THE PLAIN, THE ENEMY'S CAMPFIRES SEEMED TO OUTNUMBER THE STARS.

THEN THE WOODSMAN CUT MY POOR *GRAN* OUT OF THE WOLF, SEWED HIS *BELLY* UP WITH GREAT BOULDERS, AND TOSSED HIM IN THE RIVER, WHERE HE MOST CERTAINLY *DROWNED*.

AND SHE LIVED?

NOT FOR VERY LONG AFTER THAT. BUT SHE DIED *PEACEFULLY* ENOUGH. MY PARENTS AND YOUNGER SISTERS WERE KILLED WHEN THE INVADERS CAME. THEY KEPT ME ALIVE, AS A SOLDIERS' *PRIZE* FIRST, AND AFTER THAT AS A SCRUB WOMAN IN THE DISTRICT GOVERNOR'S PALACE.

OH DEAR.

AS THE YEARS PASSED, I BECAME JUST ANOTHER ONE OF THE *FURNISHINGS*. THEY GRADUALLY GREW TO TRUST ME ENOUGH NOT TO WATCH ME *TOO* CLOSELY. WHEN AN OPPORTUNITY PRESENTED ITSELF, I MADE MY ESCAPE AND EVENTUALLY FOUND MY WAY HERE.

OH, LOOK. HERE I'VE KEPT YOU *TALKING* THE NIGHT AWAY, WHEN YOU SHOULD BE *SLEEPING*.

NO, I'M NOT TIRED. *HONEST*. AND WITH WHAT WE'RE SURELY FACING TOMORROW, I COULDN'T SLEEP IF I *WANTED* TO. BUT WE SHOULD GO NOW.

YOU'VE GOT TO GET ABOARD THE SHIP SOON, TO SECURE YOUR *PLACE*.

I WILL, BUT I WANT YOU TO COME WITH ME.

WHAT DO YOU MEAN? *I'M* NOT GOING. I *CAN'T*. I WON'T EVEN BE IN THE LOTTERY.

MY PLACE IS WITH THE COLONEL.

WELL, THINK ABOUT *THIS* FOR A MOMENT.

IF YOU WERE *MARRIED*, THE COLONEL WOULD *MAKE* YOU GO, WOULDN'T HE? I'M CERTAIN I SPOTTED A PRIEST AMONG THE GARRISON.

I-- I *CAN'T*.

...MY DUTY...

LITTLE BOY BLUE -- HOW CAN THEY CALL YOU BY SUCH A NAME? IT'S *HARDLY* DESCRIPTIVE OF ONE SO LARGE IN HONOR AND VALOR.

WHAT AM I TO *DO* WITH YOU?

COME WITH ME, MY BRAVE SOLDIER.

WHERE TO?

YOUR QUARTERS. IF YOU STEADFASTLY *REFUSE* TO SLEEP, THERE'S *OTHER* USE WE CAN MAKE OF YOUR BED.

MY PLACE IN THE BOAT WILL KEEP FOR ANOTHER HOUR.

YOU NEED TO GET TO THE SHIP *NOW!*

LET ME GET MY BOOTS ON.

CARRY THEM. COME NOW, OR THEY'LL LEAVE YOU *BEHIND.*

NO... WAIT!

I DON'T WANT TO GO WITHOUT YOU. DAMN YOUR COLONEL AND DAMN YOUR STUBBORN MILITARY HONOR! SOME THINGS HAVE TO BE MORE IMPORTANT THAN DUTY!

COME WITH ME, BLUE.

OR LET ME STAY HERE WITH YOU.

NO, I HAVE TO STAY, AND YOU HAVE TO GO, BECAUSE I NEED YOU TO LIVE--TO SURVIVE THIS FOR BOTH OF US.

WHAT LITTLE COURAGE I CAN SUMMON UP TO STAY DEPENDS ON THE SURE KNOWLEDGE THAT I'VE BOUGHT YOUR LIFE BY DOING SO.

OTHERWISE THIS IS MEANINGLESS.

I'M FORTUNE'S FAVORITE SON.

GOD KEEP YOU!

WHERE THE *HELL* HAVE YOU *BEEN?*

THEY'RE OVER THE FIRST WALL.

SEEING RIDING HOOD ON HER WAY. WHAT HAPPENED?

DON'T *BLOW* THAT THING! EVERYONE'S ALREADY WHERE THEY'RE SUPPOSED TO BE--

--EXCEPT *YOU.*

I WANT YOU UP ON THE TOWER TOP, WHERE YOU CAN SEE EVERYTHING.

WHY NOT WITH YOU, SIR? DID I--?

BECAUSE I *SAID* SO. HERE, TAKE *THIS.* IT'S THE WITCHING CLOAK. *WEAR* IT.

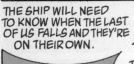

THE SHIP WILL NEED TO KNOW WHEN THE LAST OF US FALLS AND THEY'RE ON THEIR OWN.

WHEN THE ENEMY REACHES THE UPPER KEEP, WE'RE DONE HERE.

THAT'S *YOUR* JOB.

THAT'S WHEN YOU USE THE CLOAK TO *WITCH* YOURSELF ONTO THE SHIP.

BUT--

SOMEONE HAS TO DO IT, SON. I CHOSE *YOU.* DON'T SULLY A PERFECT MILITARY CAREER BY *DISOBEYING* MY FINAL ORDER.

SOMEONE HAS TO SURVIVE TO TELL OUR STORY.

VULCO TELLS ME YOU'RE SWEET ON THAT GIRL-- GO *BE* WITH HER.

"SO THAT'S HOW IT HAPPENED, WHILE EVERY-ONE ELSE *FOUGHT* AND *DIED*...

"... I STAYED IN SAFETY...

"...AND *WATCHED*.

"THE ENEMY SOLDIERS SWARMED OVER OUR WALLS ON BRIDGES OF THEIR OWN PILED DEAD.

"THEY KILLED ANCIENT *KING PELLINORE* IN HIS RUSTED ARMOR, WHICH KEPT TRYING TO FALL APART ANYWAY OVER HIS WEEKS HERE.

" WE USED TO MOCK HIS POOR *SQUIRE*, WHO HAD TO FOLLOW OLD PELLY LIKE A SHADOW, CONSTANTLY RETRIEVING THE PIECES THAT DROPPED OFF IN HIS WAKE, LIKE A CHILD SCATTERING BREAD CRUMBS BEHIND HIM.

" THEN I SAW *TAM LIN* FALL. HE HAD THE REPUTATION AS A SCOUNDREL, BUT WHEN HE'D WON A PLACE FOR HIMSELF ON THE SHIP, HE GAVE IT TO HIS YOUNG *PAGE*, TO GO IN HIS STEAD."

AND KEEP HER *WELL* AWAY FROM THOSE WALLS!

STEER *AWAY* FROM THE *PYLONS*, DAMN YOU! DO YOU WANT TO DO THE ENEMY'S *JOB FOR* HIM AND *SINK* US?

I'M *TRYING,* CAP'N, BUT SHE'S OVERLOADED AND TURNS LIKE A POX-DRUNK *WHORE.*

WHAT CAN I DO TO *HELP,* CAPTAIN?

I'M NOT THE CAPTAIN. I'M THE *OWNER.*

BUT IF YOU WANT TO HELP, FIND A BOW AND WATCH THE SKY. THEY HAVE FLYING THINGS THAT CAN BYPASS THE KEEP AND *DESTROY* US, ONCE THEY REALIZE WHERE THE GATEWAY *REALLY* IS.

JUST ABOUT *ANYTHING* CAN DESTROY US NOW.

"AT LEAST HALF OUR MEN FELL TRYING TO HOLD THE OUTER WARD. ONCE THEY WERE GONE, THE ENEMY POURED OVER THE WALL, DEFENDING THE INNER WARD WITH RELATIVE EASE.

"ROBIN'S MIRY MEN DIED BESIDE THOSE OF OUR *OWN* COMPANY, WHO DIED BESIDE THE MEN OF OTHER FAR KINGDOMS.

"ROBIN O' THE WOODS TOLD ME HE'D VOLUNTEERED TO STAY BEHIND, AS HE PUT IT, 'TO PROPERLY AVENGE MY MARIAN'.

IT LOOKS LIKE THEY'VE GOT US *CUT OFF*, LADY.

WE'RE DONE FOR, LOXLEY, BUT I HAVE ONE LAST *TASK* TO COMPLETE FIRST. CAN YOU *HOLD* THEM FOR A MOMENT?

"SHE WAS KILLED WHEN THE INVADERS TOOK HIS HOMELAND.

MY SPEAR WILL FIND ANY *TARGET* I SET FOR IT. IF THEIR GENERAL IS SOMEWHERE ON THE FIELD...

...AT LEAST THESE BEASTS WILL HAVE TO CELEBRATE THEIR SLAUGHTER *WITHOUT* HIM.

"I DON'T KNOW *WHY* THE STRANGE, DOUR WOMAN, BRITOMART, CHOSE TO STAY. I NEVER GOT TO SPEAK TO HER.

"TRUTH IS, SHE *INTIMIDATED* ME.

"ONCE THEY WERE CUT OFF, THEY DIDN'T LAST LONG.

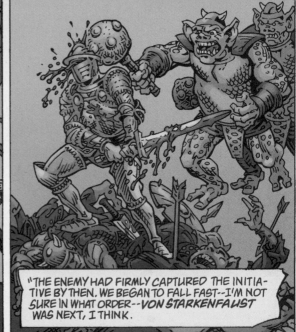

"THE ENEMY HAD FIRMLY CAPTURED THE INITIATIVE BY THEN. WE BEGAN TO FALL FAST--I'M NOT SURE IN WHAT ORDER--*VON STARKENFAUST* WAS NEXT, I THINK.

"FOLLOWED BY ROBIN'S WARRIOR MONK FRIEND.

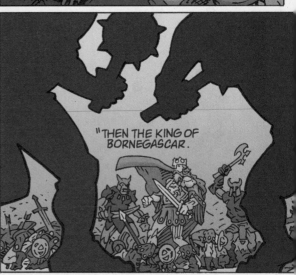

"THEN THE KING OF BORNEGASCAR.

"OR WAS IT HIS NEIGHBOR FROM MADAGAO? I COULD NEVER FIGURE OUT IF THEY WERE SWORN ENEMIES OR FAST FRIENDS. MAYBE THEY DIDN'T KNOW EITHER.

"PERHAPS IT'S ENOUGH TO SAY THAT THEY DIED WELL-- A FITTING EPITAPH FOR ALL. ROB'S FRIEND, JOHN SMALL, TOOK A SCORE OF THEM WITH HIM. HE WAS ALWAYS DRINKING AND TALKING LOUD. I LIKED HIM."

"THEN SOMETHING HAPPENED. IF NOT QUITE A *MIRACLE*, THEN SOMETHING EXTRAORDINARY. THE REDCROSS KNIGHT WAS HOLDING THE ROOF OF THE MAIN KEEP ALONE.

"AND HE COULDN'T BE BEATEN!

"NOT BY GOBLIN OR TROLL OR GIANT! NOT BY THE DOZENS OR THE HUNDREDS!

"HE LASTED FOR OVER AN HOUR AND I BEGAN TO BELIEVE HE'D WIN ALL ON HIS OWN.

"UNTIL THEY SET THE DRAGON AGAINST HIM.

"IT'S SAID HE KILLED A DRAGON ONCE."

"BUT NOT THIS TIME.

"AND FINALLY COLONEL BEARSKIN, HE TRIED TO HOLD THE UPPER KEEP, AND DID...

"...FOR A WHILE."

"I'D LIKE TO BE ABLE TO SAY THAT HE FOUGHT TO HIS LAST BREATH, BUT HE DIDN'T-- HE *COULDN'T.* A GOBLIN SWORD GUTTED HIM AND THEN THEY LEFT HIM TO DIE SLOWLY, IN AGONY.

FINISH ME, YOU *BASTARDS!*

"THEY LAUGHED AND MOCKED HIM AS HE LAY THERE, BEGGING FOR HELP, OR AT LEAST FOR A FINAL MERCY.

"HE LASTED FOR MANY HORRIBLE MINUTES THAT SEEMED TO STRETCH ON FOREVER, AS BRIGHT PINK PETALS FROM THE PEACH TREE DRIFTED DOWN ON HIM, LIKE A BLOODSTAINED SNOWFALL.

...PLEASE...

"THEN THE SOLDIERS SEEMED AS ONE TO RECALL THAT THERE WAS STILL THIS LAST TOWER TO TAKE.

"OUR DOOMED DEFENSE WAS DONE AND IT WAS TIME FOR ME TO GO."

"I WISHED MYSELF AWAY FROM THERE.

"AND IMMEDIATELY FOUND MYSELF ON BLUEBEARD'S SHIP, SQUEEZED AMONG THOSE OTHERS FATED TO LIVE.

GOOD LORD!

WHERE DID *YOU* COME FROM?

FROM *HELL*. I'VE JUST COME FROM *HELL*.

WHERE'S MISS RIDING HOOD? DOES ANYONE *KNOW*?

IS SHE BELOW DECKS?

"I DIDN'T HAVE A CHANCE THEN TO LOOK FOR HER.

WE'RE APPROACHING THE *FALLS*!

ALL HANDS, *STAND BY* ON PORT AND STAR-BOARD! PREPARE TO *DEPLOY WINGS*, AS SOON AS WE CLEAR THE CLIFFS!

"THE SHIP WAS RUSHING HEAD-LONG DOWN THE RIVER RAPIDS AND, LIKE THE OTHERS, ALL I COULD DO WAS FIND SOME-THING TO HANG ON TO."

DEPLOY!

WHERE AWAY, SKIPPER?

MAKE YOUR COURSE *EAST* OF THE SUN AND *WEST* OF THE MOON. BEST POSSIBLE SPEED.

WHAT'S THAT?

LOOKIE! SOMETHING'S *FOLLOWING* US!

"TWO MORE DRAGONS. JUST AS I'D BEGUN TO HOPE THAT WE'D MADE IT SAFELY AWAY, IT TURNED OUT THAT WE WERE DOOMED ALL ALONG TO DIE WITH THE OTHERS."

"THEN, AS THEY CLOSED WITH *US*, WE SAW SOMETHING CLOSING WITH *THEM*. SEVEN OF THE CROW BROTHERS HAD SURVIVED TO FOLLOW US!"

SPLIT UP, BROTHERS. WE NEED TO TAKE THEM BOTH AT ONCE.

SUR- PRISE IS OUR ONLY HOPE.

"THEY ATTACKED THE DRAGONS FEARLESSLY-- A FEW TINY BLADES AGAINST THE MIGHT OF THOSE GREAT BEASTS."

AND THAT'S ABOUT IT. WE GOT AWAY-- ARRIVED HERE--AND BECAME PART OF FABLETOWN.

LUCKY US.

THE END.

HOLD **ON** THERE, KIDDO. YOU DIDN'T **FINISH.**

WHAT HAPPENED TO **RIDING HOOD?** IF SHE GOT AWAY, WHY HASN'T SHE BEEN HERE **WITH** YOU ALL THESE YEARS?

WELL, THAT'S THE POINT AT WHICH THIS STORY BECOMES A RIDICULOUS **FARCE,** ISN'T IT?

A GROTESQUE PARODY OF AN INSIPID O. HENRY TALE.

"SHE NEVER GOT ON THE BOAT. I HEARD IT FROM THE MAN SHE SURRENDERED HER SPOT TO.

GO ON. I'VE DECIDED TO STAY WITH BLUE.

"SHE DIDN'T KNOW THE COLONEL HAD ALREADY MADE HIS PLAN TO **SAVE** ME, SO SHE STAYED...

"...AND **DIED...**

"...WHILE I WAS THE ONE THAT GOT AWAY."

OUT OF THE WOODS

CHAPTER ONE • MARCH OF THE WOODEN SOLDIERS

THAT'S MUCH FURTHER AWAY, BUT YOU'LL BE THERE THE FOLLOWING DAY.

WE'LL PUT YOU ON A PLANE OUT OF SASKATOON.

A PLANE? DO YOU MEAN A FLYING MACHINE? I'M ACTUALLY GOING TO *FLY*?

OF COURSE. DON'T WORRY, IT'S SAFE ENOUGH. EVERYONE DOES IT.

THEY WERE RIGHT. THIS *IS* A LAND OF MIRACLES.

YOU DON'T KNOW THE *HALF* OF IT. PEOPLE CAN TALK TO EACH OTHER FROM ACROSS THE GLOBE, FOR LESS THAN THE COST OF A SINGLE *MEAL*.

AND EVERY HOUSE HAS A BOX THAT PLAYS MUSIC AND ANOTHER BOX THAT GATHERS INFORMATION AND ANOTHER BOX FOR-- WELL, I GUESS YOU MIGHT DESCRIBE IT AS ENDLESS *PUPPET* SHOWS.

WHATEVER KIND YOU WANT, COMEDIES OR TRAGEDIES, AT THE *PUSH* OF A BUTTON.

AND NOT JUST FOR THE GENTRY. EVEN THE PEASANTRY HAS THESE THINGS.

ASTONISHING.

AND YET WE CALL THIS THE *MUNDANE* WORLD.

"*TERRIBLE* THINGS ARE ON THE WAY."

FIVE THOUSAND BOXEN GOLD COINS; TWENTY-TWO HUNDRED OF THE EMPIRE FIFTY-OUNCE GOLD TRADING BARS; SIX FULL CHESTS OF EMERALD CITY SILVER, WHICH IS STILL BEING COUNTED.

THEN THERE'RE SEPARATE CHESTS FOR LOOSE DIAMONDS, RUBIES AND EMERALDS. AN ENTIRE ROOM OF MOUNTED, FINISHED JEWELRY--

AND THE LIST GOES ON. HELL, SIR, WE'RE STILL FINDING SECRET VAULT ROOMS.

THIS PLACE IS A LABYRINTH.

MARVELOUS, ISN'T IT?

AND LOOK AT ALL OF THE MUNDY BANK ACCOUNTS HE KEPT, UNDER SO MANY IDENTITIES.

I DARE SAY OUR LATE MISTER BLUEBEARD (REST HIS SOUL) COULD HAVE BOUGHT AND SOLD EVERYONE IN FABLETOWN.

MISTER MAYOR, I NEED TO SPEAK TO YOU.

OF COURSE, BIGBY, OF COURSE. NOT NOW, THOUGH. TOO BUSY AT THE MOMENT.

NOT GOOD ENOUGH, YOUR HONOR. YOU'VE BEEN DODGING ME FOR WEEKS.

VERY WELL. I CAN SPARE YOU A FEW MINUTES. THEN BACK TO BUSINESS.

YOU LOOK LIKE HELL.

IS THAT A *MEDICAL* OPINION?

STRICTLY AN OBSERVATION, MISS WHITE.

I DIDN'T SLEEP WELL LAST NIGHT. BAD DREAMS.

KNIGHTS OF MALTA HOSPITAL

ANYTHING YOU NEED TO TELL ME ABOUT?

I WOULD IF I COULD REMEMBER, BUT IT'S ALL A BLUR. PROBABLY JUST A BIT OF BAD *PORK* I ATE YESTERDAY.

YOU CAN GET DRESSED NOW. THE PREGNANCY IS COMING ALONG FINE.

NO IT ISN'T. NOTHING IS "FINE" ABOUT IT. IT'S GOING TO RUIN MY *LIFE*, MY STANDING IN THE COMMUNITY AND WHAT'S *LEFT* OF MY REPUTATION.

IF THAT'S THE WAY YOU FEEL ABOUT IT, YOU DO HAVE *OPTIONS*. THIS IS THE TWENTY-FIRST CENTURY, AFTER ALL.

WHAT BUSINESS COULD YOU *POSSIBLY* HAVE WITH *ME?*

YOU'VE PUT BLUEBEARD BEYOND MY REACH, AND YOUR MACHINATIONS WITH OUR MAYOR HAVE MADE YOU SAFE...

...FOR NOW.

BUT NOT *YOU*, MISTER HOBBES. YOU'RE STILL INDICTABLE FOR THE PART YOU PLAYED IN THIS CONSPIRACY.

ACTUALLY, NO, HE ISN'T.

I GAVE HIM *BLANKET* AMNESTY, IN RETURN FOR HIS *INVALUABLE* HELP IN EXPOSING HIS FORMER MASTER'S *MYRIAD* DEPREDATIONS.

YOU AREN'T *AUTHORIZED* TO DO THAT.

I'M ABOUT TO BE.

HOBBES AND I ARE EMBARKING ON THE FIRST STAGES OF THAT VERY ENDEAVOR EVEN NOW.

NOW, IF YOU'LL *EXCUSE* ME, WE HAVE FIVE HUNDRED *SIGNATURES* TO COLLECT.

YOU HAVE THE VERY *BEST* OF AFTERNOONS, SHERIFF.

I KNEW YOU'D BE COMING BACK FROM YOUR DOCTOR'S APPOINT-MENT ABOUT NOW.
I TOLD YOU, I NEED TIME ALONE FOR AWHILE.
FAIR ENOUGH-- TO A POINT, BUT I CAN'T LET YOU CUT ME OUT OF THIS ENTIRELY.
FOR BETTER OR WORSE, I'M THE FATHER OF THAT CUB GROWING IN YOUR BELLY, AND AS SUCH I HAVE SOME SAY IN THE PLANS YOU MAKE, NO MATTER HOW UNCOMFORTABLE WE ARE IN EACH OTHER'S COMPANY.
I--
YOU--
YES, YOU'RE RIGHT, OF COURSE.
YOU DESERVE A SAY, AND YOU'LL HAVE IT.
WE'LL HAVE A LONG TALK, I PROMISE. BUT PLEASE--JUST GIVE ME A LITTLE MORE TIME. I'M NOT READY YET. ANOTHER DAY OR TWO.

OKAY, BUT I HAVE AN *OFFICIAL* MATTER TO DISCUSS.

COME ON, I'LL WALK YOU IN. ARE YOU GOING UPSTAIRS OR TO THE OFFICE?

OFFICE.

I'VE BEEN LETTING MY WORK SLIP OF LATE AND I NEED TO CATCH UP.

I'D PREFER YOU GO *HOME* INSTEAD, AND STRAIGHT TO BED. YOU LOOK *EXHAUSTED.*

PLEASE DON'T BE *NICE* TO ME, BIGBY. NOT RIGHT NOW. IT JUST ADDS TO THE PRESSURE.

FINE. ALL BUSINESS THEN. YOUR *EX* JUST MENTIONED SOMETHING TO ME THAT STRUCK ME AS ODD.

WHY WOULD PRINCE CHARMING NEED TO COLLECT *FIVE HUNDRED* SIGNATURES?

I'M SURE I DON'T KNOW. NO DOUBT ANOTHER *SCHEME* HE'S COOKING UP.

NO, WAIT.

OH NO. HE WOULDN'T!

WHAT?

WHAT?

COME WITH ME.

BLUE! WHERE ARE YOU?

HE'S SLEEPING, MISSY WHITE. HE WAS UP ALL NIGHT.

THAT'S FINE, BUFKIN. YOU'LL DO.

FIND ME THE VOLUME ON FABLETOWN *ELECTION* RULES.

I CAN'T DO THAT. BLUEBEARD'S *GOB* BUTLER CHECKED IT OUT SOME TIME AGO.

OH DEAR LORD.

WILL ONE OF YOU *PLEASE* TELL ME WHAT'S GOING ON?

I'M NOT CERTAIN, BECAUSE IT'S NEVER COME UP BEFORE...

...BUT IF I REMEMBER CORRECTLY, ANY FABLETOWN CITIZEN CAN CALL FOR A SPECIAL ELECTION BY COLLECTING FIVE HUNDRED FABLE SIGNATURES.

I THINK MY EX-HUSBAND PLANS TO RUN FOR *MAYOR*.

DAYS PASS AND SPRING SETTLES IN TO STAY FOR AWHILE.

SO WHAT ARE WE GOING TO DO ABOUT PRINCE CHARMING?

WHAT *CAN* WE DO? HE HAS THE LAW ON HIS SIDE.

WELL, I FOR ONE HAVE NO INTENTION OF WORKING FOR HIM. I'LL *QUIT* IF HE'S ELECTED.

WHY WOULD SOMEONE WANT TO TAKE MY PLACE?

HAVEN'T I DONE A *GOOD* JOB?

LET'S NOT JUMP THE GUN. HE HASN'T GOT THE SIGNATURES YET. BUT I SHOULD MENTION THAT, IF YOU HADN'T GIVEN HIM A FREE *PASS* ON THE BLUEBEARD MESS, WE'D HAVE MORE *OPTIONS* NOW.

TAP TAP TAP

SORRY TO INTERRUPT, BUT THERE'S QUITE A *COMMOTION* OUTSIDE--SOMETHING I THINK YOU'LL WANT TO SEE.

WHAT *NOW?*

MORE TROUBLES TO PLAGUE US, NO DOUBT.

THEY DO COME IN THREES.

SUPERSTITION.

RED, WHITE AND BLUE

CHAPTER TWO ○ MARCH OF THE WOODEN SOLDIERS

NO NEED--?

BUT I'M **WOUNDED!**

I'VE TWO POINTS WORTH MAKING, **BOTH** OF WHICH CAN BE SAID AT A REASONABLE VOLUME.

FIRST, **I'M** NOT THE ONE WHO SET UP MY WOODEN SOLDIER COLLECTION ALL OVER THE BEDROOM FLOOR.

THEY'RE THE **ONLY** POSSESSION I WAS ABLE TO BRING OUT OF THE HOMELANDS WITH ME, CARVED BY MY OWN FATHER, GEPETTO, WHO NEVER MADE IT OUT AT ALL.

AS SUCH, THEY'RE THE ONLY THINGS I HAVE TO STILL REMEMBER MY DAD, WHO FOR ALL **I** KNOW MAY BE DEAD-- OR EVEN WORSE--**ENSLAVED** ALL THESE YEARS.

FOR EXACTLY **THAT** REASON, I TREASURE THEM TOO MUCH TO TREAT AS MERE TOYS.

BUT--

BUT FLYCATCHER CAN'T SEEM TO GET THAT NOTION THROUGH HIS THICK **SKULL.**

HE'S THE ONE WHO KEEPS SNEAKING INTO OUR ROOM TO **PLAY** WITH THEM--WHICH BRINGS US NICELY TO MY **SECOND** POINT.

IF YOU WOULDN'T SLEEP UNTIL PAST **NOON** ON YOUR DAYS OFF, YOU'D HAVE BEEN UP **LONG** BEFORE FLY CAME BY TO PLAY ARMY WITH MY IRREPLACEABLE KEEPSAKES.

SPEAKING OF WHICH, FLY HAD A MESSAGE FOR YOU.

THERE'S SOME SORT OF BIG COMMOTION DOWN IN THE BUSINESS OFFICE, AND BIGBY WANTS YOU DOWN THERE AS SOON AS YOU WAKE UP.

79

"AFTER THE FALL OF THE KEEP AT WORLD'S END, I WAS CAPTURED ALIVE BY THE EMPEROR'S SOLDIERS."

"FOR A FEW WEEKS THEY USED ME LIKE SOLDIERS ALWAYS TREAT CAPTURED WOMEN."

STORM'S COMING.

BIG ONE.

BULLFINCH STREET

THEN THEY SENT ME BACK INTO SLAVERY, WHICH I ENDURED FOR ALL THESE CENTURIES. EVENTUALLY I EARNED THEIR TRUST AGAIN, AND WAS ABLE TO MAKE MY ESCAPE.

I FLED TO THE OZ GATEWAY, WHICH LINKS TO YOUR NORTHERN LAND OF KANDA.

CANADA.

TWO OF YOUR FABLE GARRISON STARTED OUT TO ACCOMPANY ME FROM THE NORTHERN GATE, BUT THEY WERE KILLED BY GOBLINS THAT AMBUSHED US.

OH, WE'VE GOT *TROUBLES!*

RIGHT HERE IN *FABLE* CITY!

IT'S *FABLE TOWN.*

WHATEVER.

BEAR'S CANDIES

FOR THE FIRST *TIME* IN OUR HISTORY, THE FABLETOWN COFFERS ARE FULL TO *OVER-FLOWING.*

THE MONEY HAS WELL AND TRULY ROLLED *IN,* BUT IS ANY OF IT ROLLING BACK *OUT* AGAIN, TO ENRICH THE LIVES OF US MERE *CITIZENS?*

NO. OF *COURSE* NOT. OUR BELOVED MAYOR--WHO MUST *STILL* THINK HE'S A KING WITH DICTATORIAL POWERS--IS HOLDING *TIGHT* TO THE COMMUNITY PURSE STRINGS.

IT'S AS THOUGH HE IMAGINES *ALL* OF THE MONEY TO BE *HIS.*

AND WHILE *HE'S* RICHER THAN *CROESUS,* WE'RE LEFT TO FEND FOR *OURSELVES,* TO FAIL OR PROSPER, WITH *NO* HELP FROM OUR ELECTED GOVERNMENT.

MEANWHILE, OUT IN THE MUNDY, *THEY'RE* TAKEN CARE OF FROM THE CRADLE TO THE GRAVE.

SHOULD YOU *GOOD* PEOPLE OF FABLETOWN SEE FIT TO ELECT ME AS YOUR *NEW* MAYOR, I'LL INSTITUTE IMMEDIATE AND *SWEEPING* CHANGES.

THE FIRST THING THE *NEW* ADMINISTRATION WILL DO IS FUND *FREE GLAMOURS* FOR ANYONE WHO NEEDS THEM.

NO MORE WILL FABLES BE SHIPPED OFF TO THE FARM JUST FOR LOOKING A *TOUCH* INHUMAN.

EDWARD BEAR'S CANDIES

AND HOW ABOUT GOVERNMENT-SPONSORED *TRANSFORMATIONS* FOR ANY FARM FABLE WHO MIGHT WANT TO END CENTURIES OF UNFAIR *CONFINEMENT* UP THERE?

TURNING THEM *HUMAN?*

WHAT IF THEY DON'T *WANNA* BE HUMAN?

I ♥ CAN...

IT WORKED FOR *BIGBY,* SO WHY NOT EVERYONE ELSE?

THEY CAN *ALWAYS* RETURN TO THE SAFETY OF THE FARM DURING THOSE TIMES WHEN THEY WANT TO RESUME BEING A PIGGY, OR DUCK, OR BILLY GOAT.

MY FELLOW CITIZENS, IT'S TIME TO MAKE A *PROACTIVE* DECISION FOR THE *FUTURE* OF FABLETOWN.

IF YOU WANT TO HELP USHER IN A NEW GOLDEN AGE, SIMPLY *SIGN* THE PETITION.

PETITION

SECURITY OFFICE

B. WOLF

BUSINESS OFFICE

S. WHITE

BIGBY, WE NEED TO *TALK.*

HOW'S BOY BLUE?

IN A MILD STATE OF SHOCK. I SENT HIM HOME FOR THE DAY.

SO WHAT'S ON YOUR *MIND,* MISS WHITE?

YOU KNOW-- OR *THINK* YOU KNOW-- SOMETHING ABOUT RED RIDING HOOD. I'D LIKE TO KNOW WHAT IT IS.

SURE. GRAB A PEW. THIS MAY TAKE A WHILE.

DO YOU KNOW WHY I TOOK EXTENDED LEAVES OF ABSENCE BACK IN 1916, AND AGAIN IN 1939?

I'M NOT AN IMBECILE. I CAN READ A CALENDAR. *EVERY-ONE* KNEW YOU SNUCK OFF TO FIGHT IN THE WARS.

YOU *SEEMED* TO WANT TO KEEP IT A BIG SECRET, SO I NEVER ASKED YOU ABOUT IT BEFORE.

I'VE OFTEN WONDERED WHY YOU DID IT. AFTER ALL, IT WASN'T *OUR* FIGHT. MUNDY BUSINESS.

A SHORT-SIGHTED WAY TO LOOK AT THINGS. A WOLF GROWS UP KNOWING HE NEEDS TO *PROTECT* HIS TERRITORY OR RISK LOSING IT.

WE'VE EACH BEEN PART OF THIS COUNTRY *FAR* LONGER THAN ANY MUNDY. SOME MIGHT REASONABLY ARGUE THAT THAT ONLY *INCREASES* OUR DUTY TO FIGHT FOR IT.

AND IN WHAT *WAY* DOES THIS PERTAIN TO THE RIDING HOOD SITUATION?

"DURING THE WARS I DID MY SHARE OF FIGHTING BEHIND ENEMY LINES--MOSTLY ON MY OWN BUT OCCASIONALLY WORKING WITH OUR COMMANDO GROUPS.

"DON'T WORRY--I NEVER REVEALED MY *TRUE* NATURE TO THEM.

"FROM TIME TO TIME WE'D FIND IT ADVANTAGEOUS TO PLACE AGENTS AMONG THE ENEMY--MOST OFTEN POSING AS DEFECTORS.

"ONE GOOD WAY TO ENSURE THOSE DEFECTORS WERE TAKEN AS LEGITIMATE WAS TO LITERALLY CHASE THEM INTO ENEMY HANDS, EVEN TO THE EXTENT OF PUTTING A BULLET OR TWO INTO THEM."

ICH BIN EIN DEUTSCHER-AMERIKANER! I DON'T WANT TO BE FIGHTING AGAINST MY OWN PEOPLE NO MORE! VERSTEHEN?

IT WAS A RISK, BUT NOTHING WAS SO CONVINCING TO THE BAD GUYS LIKE SOME POOR BASTARD WOUNDED IN THE PROCESS OF JOINING UP WITH THEM.

OH MY GOD. YOU THINK RIDING HOOD IS A *SPY*, PLACED HERE BY THE ADVERSARY.

"YOU HEARD HER STORY. A CARLOAD OF GOBLINS TRIED TO KILL HER DURING HER GETAWAY, TO KEEP HER FROM REACHING US."

PRETTY *CONVINCING*, WOULDN'T YOU SAY?

"AND BACK IN THE BATTLE OF THE KEEP AT WORLD'S END, BOY BLUE SAID SHE SHOWED UP THERE IN VERY SIMILAR CIRCUMSTANCES-- GRIEVOUSLY WOUNDED WHILE TRYING TO REACH OUR SIDE."

YOU THINK SHE WAS THE ADVERSARY'S SPY EVEN *THEN*?

THE ENEMY COMMANDER BACK THEN SWORE NO ONE WOULD BE TAKEN ALIVE WHEN THE GARRISON FELL. IN PREVIOUS BATTLES SUCH THREATS WERE *ALWAYS* CARRIED OUT.

"SO WHY DID THEY LET HER AND *ONLY* HER LIVE? DID THEY REALLY NEED ONE MORE *SCRUB* WOMAN SO DESPERATELY?"

"ALSO, THE CANADA GATE HAS BEEN BLOCKED FOR NEARLY TWO HUNDRED YEARS, AND IT WAS CLOSED FROM THE OTHER SIDE--BY THE ADVERSARY'S FORCES, NOT OURS."

SUMMON THE COURT WARLOCKS. I WANT THIS GATE SHUT DOWN BY *NIGHT-FALL.*

WHO *OPENED* IT AGAIN? AND HOW DID SHE GET AWAY FROM THE CARLOAD OF GOBLINS?

SHE *TOLD* US. SHE *DROVE* AWAY AFTER THE TWO FABLE GUARDS FELL DEFENDING HER.

YEAH, AND WHO TAUGHT HER TO *DRIVE?* AND WHO PROVIDED THE *PURSUING* GOBS WITH A CAR OF THEIR OWN?

IT WAS ALL A SETUP?

"SOMEONE IN THE HOMELANDS CAREFULLY PREPARED EVERY PLAYER TO ACT HIS PART."

ONE PEDAL IS FOR MAKING THE MACHINE *GO.* ONE MAKES IT *STOP* AND THE THIRD IS NEEDED TO CHANGE GEARS.

WHAT'S *GEARS?*

BUT THEY OVERDID IT.

THIS IS JUST SUPPOSITION, THOUGH. NONE OF IT CONSTITUTES ACTUAL *EVIDENCE*.

SURE. IT'S ALL JUST A BUNCH OF SUSPICIONS SO FAR, AND I'M *NATURALLY* SUSPICIOUS. BUT IT'S WORTH LOOKING INTO, WOULDN'T YOU AGREE?

SO WHAT ARE YOU GOING TO DO?

SNIFF AROUND.

IN THE MEANTIME, YOU NEED TO RIDE HERD ON KING COLE. HE'S A BIT *TOO* DELIGHTED WITH OUR NEW ARRIVAL--READY TO GRANT HER IMMEDIATE FABLE CITIZENSHIP.

SHE'S GOOD NEWS, AND ANY GOOD NEWS IS GOOD FOR CONTRIBUTIONS.

IT'S ALWAYS ABOUT MONEY WITH OUR MAYOR.

NO GOVERNMENT CAN WORK WITHOUT IT. YOU SHOULDN'T BE SO *QUICK* TO IMPUGN HIS CHARACTER.

POINT TAKEN.

NO, NO, NO! GET IT *STRAIGHT*, BUDDY.

THERE WERE ORIGINALLY *FIVE* MAGIC BEANS THAT MY MOTHER (GOD REST HER SOUL) THREW OUT THE WINDOW.

THEN *LATER*, AFTER MAKING SURE SHE'D FALLEN ASLEEP--SO AS TO AVOID ANOTHER BEATING-- I SNUCK OUT AND SCRAMBLED AROUND IN THE DARK TO GET THEM *BACK*.

THE GLASS SLIPPER SHOES

TAVERN

I WAS ABLE TO FIND FOUR OF THEM, BY FEEL, BEFORE GIVING UP.

AND THE NEXT DAY I DISCOVERED THAT THE MAGIC BEANSTALK HAD GROWN FROM THE ONE BEAN I *COULDN'T* FIND.

ALL THAT STALK FROM JUST ONE BEAN?

YES, THRUSHBEARD. PRECISELY. THAT'S WHAT I'VE BEEN TRYING TO GET THROUGH YOUR THICK *SKULL* ALL NIGHT.

Stop Me if You've Heard This One, But a Man Walks Into a Bar...
CHAPTER THREE ○ MARCH OF THE WOODEN SOLDIERS

99

WILL YOU POST THIS PLEASE, SQUIRE VULCO?

UHM... SURE. WHY NOT?

THIS IS THE PLACE, BROTHERS.

WHEN DOES IT OPEN, BROTHERS?

IN MERE MOMENTS.

THREE FLOORS OF GUNS!

MY ANTICIPATION IS *VAST*, BROTHERS--THOUGH I WISH WE COULD HAVE RETURNED TO THE WAREHOUSE FOR A NEW *LEG* BEFORE VENTURING HERE.

IT'S A MATTER OF CONSERVING EFFORT, BROTHER. WE HAVE TO TAKE OUR PURCHASES BACK TO THE WAREHOUSE ANYWAY, SO WHY MAKE *TWO* TRIPS?

AS ALWAYS, BROTHER, YOUR REASONING IS *FLAWLESS*.

BIGGEST GUN STORE IN BROOKLYN

BIG NED'S DISCOUNT GUNS
SINCE 1968
I don't want a lot of money, because I just love selling guns! Your gain!

THE WOODLAND, NEW YORK CITY.

AS YOU CAN SEE, ONE OF THEM HAD A WOODEN LEG.

I PICKED IT UP IN HOPES OF BEING ABLE TO *BEAT* THE BASTARDS TO DEATH WITH IT.

BUT THEY GOT AWAY.

SO WHAT'S YOUR *SCAM,* JACK?

WHAT DO YOU MEAN?

I DON'T BELIEVE YOU GOT MUGGED. YOU'RE *UP* TO SOMETHING AND I DON'T HAVE TIME FOR IT.

I'M NOT! *LOOK* AT ME!

YOU'RE LYING NOW, BECAUSE YOU *ALWAYS* LIE.

NOT *THIS* TIME!

JACK, DID YOU EVER HEAR ABOUT THE BOY WHO CRIED WOLF?

SURE, SNOW. HE LIVES UP ON THE SEVENTH FLOOR. SO WHAT?

NEVER MIND.

MY CAB'S WAITING. I HAVE TO GO.

THEY WERE *FABLES*, BIGBY! NEW FABLES IN FABLETOWN!

HOW SO?

BECAUSE OTHERWISE THEY WOULDN'T HAVE BEEN ABLE TO WALK AWAY FROM THE BEATING I HANDED OUT.

SURE, JACK. YOU CERTAINLY LOOK LIKE YOU GOT THE BETTER OF THEM.

HOW MANY **KINDS** OF GUNS HAVE YOU MEATHEADS CREATED?

THOUSANDS.

HUNDREDS OF THOUSANDS?

THAT'S EXTRAVAGANCE **BEYOND** CREDULITY.

ARE THERE REALLY THAT MANY **DIFFERENT** KINDS OF PEOPLE YOU NEED TO KILL?

AND WHAT ABOUT BOMBS? WHERE DO WE GET THOSE?

DO WE ALSO BUY THEM HERE, OR ARE BOMBS SOLD IN A DIFFERENT SHOP?

I DON'T--

TIME IS FLEETING, BROTHERS. WE SHOULD TAKE THESE AND BE ON OUR WAY.

OH, YOU CAN'T TAKE THOSE WITH YOU **TODAY**, GENTLEMEN.

"WELL, HE SUFFERED FOR THOSE PARTICULAR CRIMES. YOU CUT HIS BELLY OPEN AND SEWED IT UP WITH ROCKS--AND THEN THREW HIM IN THE LAKE TO DROWN."

ONLY TO DISCOVER NOW THAT HE *ESCAPED* THAT FATE.

NOT EASILY. HE TOLD ME THE WHOLE STORY LAST NIGHT. IT TOOK HIM THREE *WEEKS* TO PASS THOSE STONES--ENOUGH OF THEM TO SWIM BACK TO THE SURFACE.

IT'S ONLY BECAUSE OF WHO HIS *FATHER* WAS THAT HE WAS ABLE TO HOLD HIS *BREATH* FOR SO LONG.

FINE, BUT YOU'RE MISSING THE *POINT.* I NEED SOMEONE TO *CHAMPION* MY CAUSE-- TO OFFSET HIS POSITION AGAINST ME.

I NEED YOU ONCE AGAIN TO ACT AS MY KNIGHT IN SHINING ARMOR.

OF COURSE. *ANYTHING.* BUT EVEN WITHOUT MY HELP, YOU'RE CERTAIN TO BE INVITED INTO THE COMMUNITY. IT'S JUST A MATTER OF SLOGGING THROUGH THE RED TAPE.

THE ONLY THING THAT MIGHT TAKE ANY REAL TIME IS YOUR PRE-INDUCTION INTERROGATION--MORE OF AN INTERVIEW, REALLY.

EVERYONE HAS TO DIVULGE AS MUCH AS POSSIBLE ABOUT THEIR PAST, IN ORDER TO GATHER INTELLIGENCE ABOUT THE HOME-LANDS.

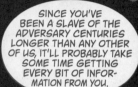

SINCE YOU'VE BEEN A SLAVE OF THE ADVERSARY CENTURIES LONGER THAN ANY OTHER OF US, IT'LL PROBABLY TAKE SOME TIME GETTING EVERY BIT OF INFORMATION FROM YOU.

THAT'S WHERE YOU CAN BE THE *MOST* HELP.

THINGS WOULD GO SMOOTHER IF I KNEW MORE ABOUT WHAT I'M *FACING.*

TELL ME ABOUT THE FARM. WHO'S UP THERE? AND WHAT MAGIC ITEMS DO YOU PEOPLE POSSESS, AND WHERE ARE THEY STORED? IT LOOKED LIKE MANY OF THEM WERE IN THE BUSINESS OFFICE.

BUT--

AND HOW MANY WITCHES, WARLOCKS AND SORCERERS DO YOU--DO *WE* HAVE HERE?

RIDE, YOU DON'T NEED TO KNOW ANY OF THAT TO JOIN FABLE-TOWN.

THIS ISN'T LIKE U.S. NATURALIZATION, WHERE YOU'LL BE QUIZZED ABOUT DETAILS OF THE CONSTITUTION AND GOVERNMENT ORGANIZATION BEFORE YOU CAN BE SWORN IN.

ACTUALLY, WANTING TO KNOW THAT KIND OF STUFF WILL MAKE BIGBY *MORE* SUSPICIOUS.

OH, POOH ON THAT FLEA-BITTEN OLD MONSTER. I'M TIRED OF TALKING ABOUT HIM.

LET'S TALK ABOUT YOU AND ME AND WHY YOU HAVEN'T EVEN *KISSED* ME YET.

WHO **ARE** YOU?

I KNOW YOU AREN'T RIDING HOOD.

CARE TO TELL ME WHAT YOU *DID* WITH HER?

I WARNED YOU I'D CHANGED. *CENTURIES* OF TORTURE--

DON'T EVEN *TRY* THAT WITH ME, LADY. JUST TELL ME WHO YOU ARE, BEFORE I TURN YOU IN.

AND WHAT'S WITH THIS PLACE?

MIND YOUR *MANNERS*, YOUNG MAN.

I WON'T BE *ADDRESSED* WITH SUCH CONTEMPT.

AHHHHH!

SHALL WE KILL HIM, MISTRESS?

NEXT:
WICKED

SUNRISE AT FABLETOWN'S UPSTATE FARM ANNEX.

3 PiGS ESQUIRE

TRACTOR MAINTAINANCE

The **Letter**

Chapter Five of March of the Wooden Soldiers

~YAWN~

KAY-EYE-ESS-ESS-EYE-EN-GEE! ♪

YOU COULD BE SANDWICHES BY *LUNCHTIME*, KID.

GOOD MORNING, STINKY. DID YOU SLEEP WELL?

OFFICE

SO, *YOU'RE* GOING TO START CALLING ME THAT, TOO?

LOVELY!

GOOD MORNING, MISS RED.

...MMHM-HMM...

YOU LOOK LIKE YOU SLEPT IN THE BARN.

FOR AN HOUR OR TWO. WEYLAND SMITH AND I WERE WORKING ON THE TRACTOR ALL NIGHT.

OH?

REALLY?

♪ ROSE AND WEYLAND, SITTING IN A TREE-- ♪

I FELL DOWN MISSY SKUNK'S HOLE *ONCE!* THAT SHOULDN'T BE ENOUGH TO WARRANT SUCH A DISREPUTABLE NICKNAME.

SUCH ARE THE GLORIES AND TRIBULATIONS OF INTERSPECIES ROMANCE.

WHAT ROMANCE? I FELL! SHE'S A *SKUNK!*

GOOD MORNING, PETE. THE DAY SHIFT HAS ARRIVED. YOU CAN TUCK YOURSELF BACK INTO YOUR MUSTARD POT NOW.

SURE, YOU BET... :YAWN:... SEE YOU THIS EVENING.

WHY ARE THERE SO MANY **NEW** ENTRIES ON THE DAILY INCIDENT BLOTTER?

BECAUSE THERE WERE LOTS OF **COMPLAINTS** LAST NIGHT. I GUESS I SHOULD'VE MENTIONED THAT, HUH?

"I HAD TO WRITE ALL NIGHT JUST TO KEEP **UP** WITH THEM."

1:06 A.M.
Miss Mousey complained about the...

IT WAS THAT BIG CHICKEN-LEGGED THINGY-- THAT BABY YOGI'S MAGIC HUT.

BABA YAGA.

YEAH, SURE-- **THAT** THING. ANYWAY, IT WAS RUNNING AROUND ALL NIGHT, OUT OF CONTROL--

--STEPPING ON PEOPLE'S ROOFS, TURNING OVER GARBAGE CANS, SCATTERING THE MUNDY HERDS AND FLOCKS.

BUT IT CAN'T **DO** THAT. IT'S UNDER OUR CONTROL. SOME OF THE MORE **EXPENSIVE** SPELLS WE BUY ARE LAID OVER THAT WRETCHED OLD WITCH'S HUT.

WHY DIDN'T YOU **WAKE** ME?

WHO COULD **FIND** YOU? YOU WEREN'T IN YOUR ROOM LAST NIGHT.

OH, REALLY?

NEVER MIND ABOUT THAT. WHERE IS IT **NOW?**

THAT CAME AS QUITE A SHOCK TO ME, AS WELL.

BUT WHAT CAN WE *DO*? SOMETIMES OUR INTELLIGENCE SERVICES CAN'T BE ALL ONE EXPECTS.

WE'D *HOPED* I COULD MAINTAIN THIS IDENTITY AMONG YOU FABLETOWN REFUGEES FOR *YEARS* TO COME.

BUT IN QUICK SUCCESSION, I RAN INTO TWO FABLES--YOU AND THE WOLF--WHO KNEW THE ORIGINAL RIDE WELL ENOUGH TO *EXPOSE* ME. BAD LUCK.

SO, I'M RELUC-TANTLY FORCED TO *ABANDON* SUBTERFUGE IN FAVOR OF ONE OF OUR ALTERNATE PLANS OF ACTION.

I DON'T THINK HE CAN *HEAR* YOU, MISTRESS.

MIND YOUR-SELVES!

HE'S CONSCIOUS-- BARELY. YOUR WOODEN SENSES AREN'T AS *ACUTE* AS MINE, HUGH.

INSULTING US, MISTRESS?

THAT'S UNCALLED FOR. TRUE, WE MAY BE UNDER YOUR ORDERS ON THIS *PARTICULAR* MISSION.

BUT NEVER FORGET THAT *WE'RE* THE CHOSEN ELITE OF THE EMPIRE.

TRUE *SONS* OF THE EMPEROR.

CARVED IN HIS IMAGE.

WE WON'T BE INSULTED BY MEAT, NO MATTER *HOW* LOFTY THE PARTICULAR PIECE OF MEAT.

UNDER-STAND ME, GENTLE-MEN?

FORGIVE US, DREAD MISTRESS.

WE MIS-SPOKE.

WE PAUSE TO REMIND OUR-SELVES THAT YOU'RE OUR EMPEROR'S MOST TREASURED LADY.

AND HUMBLY BESEECH YOUR PARDON.

WHAT ARE YOUR ORDERS?

SINCE YOU'VE EMPTIED THIS TWITCHING CARCASS OF USEFUL INFORMATION, SHALL WE FINISH HIM FOR YOU?

CHOP HIM UP FOR YOUR STEWPOT?

NO, I PREFER THE MORE *TENDER* FLESH OF THE MUNDY *BABIES* YOU'VE BEEN PROVIDING.

THEY'RE ALARMINGLY EASY TO SNATCH IN *THIS* CITY.

I'VE THOUGHT OF ONE *FURTHER* USE FOR OUR MOST IMPRESSIVE BOY BLUE.

NOT SINCE WE WERE STILL AN ENGLISH COLONY AND OUR CLOSE NEIGHBORS DIDN'T NUMBER IN THE *MILLIONS*.

HOW COULD WE POSSIBLY *HIDE* THIS FROM THE MUNDYS?

I DON'T REMEMBER WHAT WE'RE SUPPOSED TO DO IN AN INVASION!

DO *YOU*?

DOES *ANY-BODY*?

OH DEAR. THIS IS *TERRIBLE.* FIRST THING WE NEED TO DO IS SUSPEND ALL *ELECTIONS.*

WHERE'S BIGBY?

WASN'T *HE* ALWAYS IN CHARGE DURING THE PAST WAR-GAMES DRILLS?

FINE, SO WE GOT *COMPLACENT.* WHEN THE ADVERSARY DIDN'T INVADE IN THE FIRST YEARS, WE FOOLISHLY BEGAN TO BELIEVE HE *NEVER* WOULD.

BUT WE'RE NOT BEING ATTACKED THIS VERY SECOND. WE'VE GOT TIME TO *PREPARE.* WE'RE NOT HELPLESS, AND WE *AREN'T* GOING TO LOSE OUR HEADS.

NOW, LISTEN *UP* FOR YOUR ASSIGNMENTS. WE'VE GOT TO GO THROUGH THIS QUICKLY, SO I CAN GET UP TO THE THIRTEENTH FLOOR FOR A MEETING WITH THE WITCHES COUNCIL.

FIRST, THE FOLLOWING PEOPLE WILL MAN THE PHONES-- COORDINATING PREPARATIONS WITH THE FARM--

BLAM!

THAT *SOUNDED* LIKE A--

WAS THAT A *SHOT?*

BUSINESS OFFICE

S. WHITE

THEY'RE *BACK!*

YOU DIDN'T *BELIEVE* ME, AND NOW THEY'RE *BACK,* AND THEY *SHOT* TRUSTY JOHN!

WHAT HAVE YOU MONSTERS *DONE* TO HIM?

DON'T INSULT US, WOMAN! *RESPECT* YOUR BETTERS.

AFTER ALL, HE'S JUST MORE DISPOSABLE *MEAT*-- EVENTUAL FOOD FOR GRUBS AND WORMS

WE'RE HERE TO DELIVER A MESSAGE-- A VERY *IMPORTANT* LETTER.

STAND BACK AND LISTEN--WITH APPROPRIATE SILENCE AND AWE.

"TO OUR SUBJECTS IN FABLETOWN AND THROUGHOUT THE MUNDANE WORLD."

"GREETINGS, FROM YOUR EMPEROR."

DEAR GOD! THE *ADVERSARY!*

"LIKE THE PRODIGAL'S FATHER, OUR LOVE FOR YOU ENDURES WITH- OUT CEASING. WITH MEASURE- LESS CHARITY, WE LONG FOR THE DAY WHEN YOU'RE GATHERED BACK UNTO OUR BOSOM."

"BUT DO NOT FRET THAT WE INTEND TO RETURN YOU TO US THROUGH FORCE. OUR EYES ARE TURNED ELSEWHERE FOR NOW, TO OTHER DISTANT FABLE LANDS, STILL IGNORANT OF THE EMPIRE'S MANIFEST BLESSINGS."

"OUR FERVENT WISH IS TO LEAVE YOU, PEACEFUL IN YOUR SELF-IMPOSED EXILE, UNTIL SUCH TIME AS YOU AWAKEN TO YOUR OWN FOLLY AND REJOIN US WILLINGLY."

"IN FURTHERANCE THEREOF, I SEND YOU OUR IMPERIAL ENVOY, A GREAT LADY OF OUR COURT, COMMONLY KNOWN AS RED RIDING HOOD. UNDER OUR PROTECTION, SHE SPEAKS WITH OUR VOICE."

"SHE WILL WORK TIRELESSLY TO ACHIEVE RECON-CILIATION BETWEEN US."

"BUT, IN THE MEANTINE, WE CAN'T LET YOU REMAIN A THORN IN OUR SIDE--A DISTRAC-TION FROM OTHER MATTERS OF CONCERN."

"THEREFORE, IN ONE DAY, A TROOP OF OUR IMPERIAL AGENTS WILL ARRIVE, TO TAKE POSSESSION OF ALL MAGIC PROPERTY ILLEGALLY REMOVED FROM OUR LANDS."

"TAKE NOTE THAT SUCH ITEMS ARE KNOWN TO US, IN DETAIL."

"IF YOU ATTEMPT TO HIDE THESE THINGS, EVEN IN YOUR HEARTS, THERE WILL WE RAKE FOR THEM, IN THE FULL-NESS OF OUR POWER AND WRATH."

EVERYONE STAY INSIDE UNTIL WE'VE LONG DEPARTED.

UNLESS YOU WISH TO RECEIVE TRULY PROMISCUOUS AMOUNTS OF GUNFIRE.

REMEMBER! YOU HAVE ONLY TWENTY-FOUR HOURS!

THEY WERE PINOCCHIOS! ALL THREE OF THEM, GODDAMNED *PINOCCHIOS!* WOODEN FUCKING *DOLLS!*

NO *WONDER* I COULDN'T HURT THEM!

NOT NOW, JACK.

FOR *ONCE* IN YOUR LIFE, SHOW SOME SENSE OF THE MOMENT.

FLYCATCHER-- CHARMING--DRIVE BLUE AND JOHN TO THE *HOSPITAL--* IMMEDIATELY.

WE'LL LET DOCTOR SWINEHEART KNOW YOU'RE ON THE WAY.

THEN GET BACK HERE AS SOON AS YOU CAN. WE HAVE MUCH TO DO.

163

THE HOSPITAL CALLED. BOY BLUE'S STILL ALIVE.

PINOCCHIO, DID YOU *HEAR* ME?

THEY THINK HE'LL BE OKAY.

YEAH, FLY, I HEARD. THAT'S GREAT NEWS.

HEY, WHAT'RE YOU DOING?

PACKING. YOU HEARD WHAT THEY SAID. I HAVE TO GO WITH THEM IN ORDER TO PREVENT A WAR.

BUT THEY'RE JUST THREE WOODEN DOLLS. WE CAN TAKE THEM *EASY*.

THREE THAT WE *KNOW* OF. AND NOTHING ABOUT THEM WILL BE EASY. REMEMBER, I USED TO BE ONE. THEY'RE TOUGH, STRONG, NEED NO FOOD, NOR SLEEP, AND FEEL NO PAIN.

WE'RE IN *BIG* TROUBLE.

BESIDES, I HAVE TO GO ANYWAY. DON'T YOU REALIZE WHAT THEIR EXISTENCE *MEANS*?

THE ADVERSARY'S LIVING WOODEN SOLDIERS *PROVE* MY DAD'S ALIVE. HE'S BEEN *MAKING* THEM.

PAPA GEPETTO IS THE ADVERSARY'S *SLAVE*.

NEXT: CALL TO ARMS!

164

WE'RE ON OUR WAY, SNOW.

WE'VE SCROUNGED UP EVERY PIECE OF ROLLING EQUIP-MENT WE COULD BEG, BORROW OR *STEAL*, AND STUFFED THEM FULL OF FARM FABLES AND GUNS--LOTS OF GUNS.

TONS OF GUNS.

AND NOW WE'RE HAULING ASS TO THE CITY-- SO HOLD ON, 'CAUSE THE CAVALRY'S COMING.

WHERE ARE WE? I CAN'T SEE!

NO, BUT YOU'RE GOING TO GET US *ALL* IN TROUBLE IF SOME MUNDY DRIVER SEES *YOU*, SO SIT BACK DOWN AND COVER *UP*, STINKY!

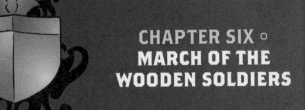

ARE WE *REALLY* GOING TO WAR, WEYLAND?

I'D LIKE TO THINK NOT. I WANT TO HOPE IT'S A BIG MISTAKE, OR AN UNANNOUNCED DRILL.

BUT THE TRUTH IS, *YES.* I DO BELIEVE WE ARE.

BUT WHY *US,* POPS?

WHY'D WE VOLUNTEER TO GO ALONG? PUT OUR *LIVES* ON THE LINE TO HELP FABLES WHO'VE GOT US PULLING PLOWS IN THE FIELDS TWELVE HOURS A DAY?

WHICH WE'LL HAVE TO *CONTINUE* DOING FOR ANOTHER 98 YEARS, BOO, UNLESS WE DEMONSTRATE OUR RE-NEWED LOYALTY TO THE POWERS THAT BE.

PROBLEM SOLVED. AND HOW GOES *YOUR* PART OF THE STRUGGLE, GENTLEMEN?

WE'RE DOING OKAY, MISTER PRINCE, SIR.

IT'S A BIT *MESSY* ROLLING THE BARRELS INTO POSITION BEFORE THE CEMENT'S FULLY SET, BUT...

MARVELOUS. YOU'RE DOING *FINE*. BY NOON WE'LL HAVE WALLS CLOSING OFF EACH END OF BULLFINCH STREET, TWO BARRELS HIGH AND AT LEAST TWO BARRELS DEEP.

WALK WITH ME, FLY.

UH.... SURE.

WHO OWNS THESE CARS? ARE THEY OURS?

YES, SIR. THEY BELONG TO FABLETOWN RESIDENTS. WE HAVE SPELLS THAT KEEP THE MUNDYS FROM PARKING HERE.

GOOD. WE'LL MOVE THEM INTO A TIGHT SEMICIRCLE HERE, TO FORM AN INNER BARRIER, DEFENDING THE WOODLAND ENTRANCE.

THIS TYPE OF WARFARE'S ALL ABOUT PREPARING A SERIES OF DEFENSIBLE FALL-BACK POSITIONS NESTED WITHIN EACH OTHER.

WE'LL USE THE WALLED COURTYARD FRONTING THE WOODLAND BUILDING AS OUR FINAL REDOUBT.

THIS IS A LOT OF WORK TO DEFEND OURSELVES AGAINST THREE WOODEN GUNMEN, *ISN'T* IT?

THREE THAT WE *KNOW* OF.

BUT WHO KNOWS HOW MANY THERE TRULY ARE?

PAY CAREFUL ATTENTION, BROTHERS.

FIRST, TAKE EXTRA CARE ON OPENING EACH CRATE, SO AS NOT TO DAMAGE THE PRECIOUS CONTENTS WITHIN.

THEN EXAMINE EACH PIECE, AS YOU UNPACK IT, TO MAKE SURE IT'S PROPERLY INTACT AND FUNCTIONAL.

I CAUTION YOU TO BE *MOST* CAREFUL WITH THE HEAD AND HANDS--

--THE THREE PARTS CARVED BY THE CREATOR HIMSELF AND ENCHANTED TO PASS AS LIVING FLESH AMONG THE MEATHEADS.

BROTHER LOU. HOW *GRAND* TO SEE YOU AGAIN!

GREETINGS, BROTHER RANDOLPH. I TRUST YOU FARED WELL DURING THESE LONG DAYS OF TRANSIT AND STORAGE?

EXTREMELY WELL, BROTHER. IN FACT I'M ALMOST LOATH TO LEAVE THE WARM AND WOMBY COMFORT OF MY COZY PACKING CRATE.

WHAT ARE YOU DOING OUT OF *BED*, YOUNG MAN?

I'M SIGNING MYSELF OUT AND GOING BACK TO FABLE-TOWN.

THERE'S A *BATTLE* COMING, DOCTOR SWINEHEART, AND I HAVE NO INTENTION OF SITTING THIS ONE *OUT*.

NONSENSE. YOU'RE IN *NO* SHAPE TO--

GET WELL BLUE

Knights of malt: HOSPITAL

LOOK AT *ME!* LOOK AT WHAT SHE DID TO MY *HANDS!*

DO YOU THINK I'LL *EVER* BE ABLE TO PLAY THE TRUMPET AGAIN WITH THESE?

I'M THE WORLD'S MOST *GIFTED* SURGEON. ONCE I'VE OPERATED, THERE'S A *GOOD* CHANCE YOU'LL RECOVER MOST OF YOUR--

BITCH IS GOING TO *PAY!*

UH, MAYBE I SHOULD DRESS FIRST.

I'D **LOVE** TO BE ABLE TO USE YOU IN THE ACTUAL FIGHTING.

UNFORTUNATELY, YOUR CONSIDERABLE POWERS WILL BE NEEDED IN A MORE **VITAL** CAPACITY.

EVEN IF WE WIN THE **BATTLE**, WE'LL STILL LOSE **EVERYTHING** IF THE MUNDYS DISCOVER **ANY** PART OF WHAT'S ABOUT TO OCCUR.

I WON'T **ALLOW** THAT. I'VE PUT TOO MANY **YEARS** INTO BUILDING FABLE-TOWN TO LOSE IT ALL NOW.

YOUR ONE AND ONLY **JOB** IS TO KEEP THE MUNDYS FROM NOTICING, OR RE-MEMBERING, ANYTHING THAT HAPPENS HERE OVER THE NEXT COUPLE OF DAYS.

THAT'S GOING TO BE AWFULLY **EXPENSIVE**, MISS WHITE. CAN FABLETOWN **AFFORD** SO MANY COSTLY ENCHANTMENTS?

THIS IS AN OFFICIALLY DECLARED FABLETOWN *EMERGENCY*, AND LIKE EVERY OTHER ABLE-BODIED FABLE, YOU'VE BEEN *DRAFTED* TO DO YOUR PART.

GO READ YOUR COPIES OF THE *FABLETOWN COMPACT*. FOR THE DURATION OF THIS CRISIS, YOU'RE WORKING FOR *FREE*.

FINE. WE'RE EAGER TO HELP.

GREAT! THEN LET'S DISCUSS THE SPECIFICS OF WHAT YOU'LL DO.

LOCK UP YOUR SONS AND DAUGHTERS, BOYS! THE *FARM FABLES* HAVE ARRIVED!

HELLO, MISS RED! WE'VE *MISSED* YOU DOWN IN THE TOWN.

ME TOO, FLY. I'VE FORGOTTEN WHAT A GORGEOUS *LADYKILLER* YOU ARE. GOOD THING I'M SITTING, BECAUSE MY KNEES HAVE SUDDENLY GONE ALL WOBBLY.

SPEAKING OF LADYKILLERS, I UNDERSTAND WE'VE *YOU* TO THANK FOR RIDDING US OF BLUEBEARD. WELL *DONE*, PRINCE CHARMING.

GLAD TO DO IT. JUST REMEMBER ME COME ELECTION DAY.

SO WHERE DO YOU WANT US, COWBOY?

UNLOAD EVERYTHING DIRECTLY INSIDE THE WOODLAND'S COURTYARD.

THAT'S GOING TO PLAY *HELL* WITH TRUSTY JOHN'S GARDEN.

HE WON'T COMPLAIN. HE'S STILL IN THE HOSPITAL, AFTER BEING *SHOT* LAST NIGHT.

MAKE SURE EVERYONE GETS ONE OF THESE RADIOS.

EVERYONE? THERE'S NOT ENOUGH, MISS WHITE. THE LOCAL RADIO SHACK ONLY HAD TWELVE IN STOCK.

NOT EVERYONE, BUT EVERY--WHAT DO WE CALL THEM? GROUP LEADERS?

PLATOON LEADERS?

SECTION LEADERS?

CHRIST ABOVE! WE DON'T EVEN HAVE A COMMON *LANGUAGE* FOR THIS BUSINESS. HOW ARE WE GOING TO EVEN PRETEND TO FUNCTION ONCE THE ACTUAL FIGHTING STARTS?

JUST DON'T SHOW INDECISION IN FRONT OF THE TROOPS AND YOU'LL DO FINE.

DOCTOR SWINEHEART? BLUE?

WHAT IN GOD'S NAME ARE YOU TWO *DOING* HERE?

DELIVERING MEDICAL SUPPLIES, AS ORDERED.

AND, OF COURSE, REPORTING FOR DUTY.

NOT THAT. WHAT IS BLUE DOING OUT OF THE HOSPITAL? AND WHAT ARE *YOU* DOING *TO* HIM?

ISN'T IT OBVIOUS? I'M TAPING THIS WEAPON TO HIS HANDS. THEY'RE SO INJURED HE COULDN'T HOLD IT OTHERWISE.

BUT HE'S NOT FIT FOR--BLUE, YOU GET BACK TO BED THIS *INSTANT!*

I'M STAYING.

SWINEHEART, YOU'RE A DOCTOR! HOW COULD YOU BE A PARTY TO THIS NONSENSE?

BECAUSE I'M A *BATTLEFIELD* SURGEON--THE BEST IN THE HISTORY OF WARFARE.

OUR PRIORITIES DIFFER FROM THOSE IN STRICTLY CIVILIAN PRACTICE, IN THAT WE'RE OFTEN CALLED UPON TO GET SOLDIERS PATCHED UP, JUST ENOUGH TO GET THEM BACK INTO THE FIGHT.

I'M ADAMANT, MISS WHITE. I *WON'T* SIT THIS OUT.

WE'RE ALL LUNATICS IN A BEDLAM!

HURRY ALONG THEN, GENTLEMEN, AND YOU CAN HEAR ME ADDRESS THE TROOPS.

CHANCES ARE, AS SOON AS THEY SEE OUR NUMBERS, THE MEATHEADS WILL SIMPLY ROLL OVER AND SHOW *THROAT*.

ONCE THEY SURRENDER, WE MUST SHOW PROPER RESTRAINT AND NOT KILL *TOO* MANY OF THEM.

PERHAPS ONLY THOSE WHO HESITATE TO OBEY.

OR FAIL TO SHOW TOTAL DEFERENCE.

FORM RANKS AND PREPARE TO MOVE *OUT!*

OR COWER AND CRINGE JUST A *BIT* TOO RELUCTANTLY.

MY DEAR BROTHERS OF THE HOLY GROVE--WE'RE ABOUT TO EMBARK ON A *GLORIOUS* ADVENTURE, IN SERVICE TO THE EMPEROR.

WOULD YOU MIND TELLING ME WHAT YOU'RE UP TO?

EXACTLY WHAT SNOW *ORDERED* ME TO DO, PINOCCHIO.

MY JOB'S TO LOOK AFTER YOU, DURING THE FIGHT.

SO THAT'S WHAT I'M PREPARING TO DO.

I DON'T NEED "LOOKING AFTER," JACK, FOR TWO VERY GOOD REASONS.

FIRST, EVEN IF THE WOODEN SOLDIERS ATTACK EVERYONE ELSE, THEY WON'T HARM ME.

DIDN'T YOU HEAR WHAT THEY SAID LAST NIGHT?

I'M THEIR EXTRA-SPECIAL SUPER-DELUXE *BIG BROTHER.*

OKAY, NOT SO MUCH "BIG," BUT THEIR TREASURED *ELDER* BROTHER.

AND SECOND, WHEN THEY GIVE UP AND RUN AWAY, I PLAN TO VOLUNTARILY GO *WITH* THEM.

SOMEWHERE OVER THERE, THE ADVERSARY HAS MY DAD *PRISONER,* TURNING OUT WOODEN SOLDIERS FOR HIM.

ALL THIS TIME I THOUGHT GEPETTO WAS *DEAD,* BUT NOW WE CAN BE *REUNITED.*

AND BESIDES, DO YOU ACTUALLY THINK YOU'LL BE ABLE TO HARM THEM WITH BULLETS?

THEY'RE *WOODEN SOLDIERS*, MORON--AS IN: MADE OF *WOOD*!

EVER SHOOT A *TREE* AND SEE IT FALL OVER DEAD?

SHOOT AT THESE GUYS ALL *DAY*, JACKASS, AND THEY WON'T FEEL A THING.

THINK YOU'VE GOT IT ALL FIGURED OUT, RUNT?

DO YOU HONESTLY IMAGINE THERE'S A CHANCE WE'D EVER LET YOU SKIP BACK TO THE HOMELANDS, TO SPILL YOUR *GUTS* TO THE ENEMY?

WHEN SNOW ORDERED ME TO "LOOK OUT FOR YOU," SHE DIDN'T NECESSARILY MEAN "PROTECT" YOU.

MY SWORD'S FOR CHOPPING UP YOUR BROTHERS IN THE KNOTHEAD BRIGADE.

BUT IF IT LOOKS LIKE YOU'RE ABOUT TO FALL INTO THEIR HANDS, AND THERE'S NO OTHER CHOICE, I HAVE THE GUN TO--

KILL ME?

BULL'S-EYE.

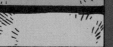

KEEP *FIRING!* POUR IT ON!

WHY? IT'S NOT DOING ANY GOOD! BULLETS DON'T SEEM TO *BOTHER* THEM!

THEN AIM AT THEIR *HEADS!* MAYBE WE CAN SHOOT THEIR *EYES* OUT, OR SPLINTER THEM SO BADLY THEY'RE *BLINDED!*

OH YEAH? AND JUST *WHEN* DO YOU THINK I BECAME ANNIE OAKLEY?

THE SOUTH WALL IS HOLDING-- FOR NOW--BUT IT WON'T MUCH LONGER, UNLESS WE REINFORCE IT. PULL ONE-IN-THREE FROM THE NORTH WALL AND--

--NO, WAIT! *CANCEL* THAT ORDER!

SMALL ARMS AREN'T HAVING MUCH *EFFECT,* MISS SNOW.

"WE WANT THEM TO OCCUPY BULLFINCH STREET, BEFORE WE REALLY START FIGHTING, BECAUSE THE LESS OF THIS THE MUNDYS SEE, THE LESS WE'LL HAVE TO COVER UP LATER.

THEY'VE DONE IT! THEY'VE MADE A *BREACH!*

"ALL PART OF THE PLAN, FLY. NO NEED TO LOSE OUR NERVE--YET."

FALL *BACK! FALL BACK!*

FLY, TELL SNOW SHE'S *GOT* TO PULL THEM OFF THE NORTH WALL TOO, OR THEY'LL BE CUT *OFF!*

NOW, FLY, WHILE THEY'RE OCCUPIED, PULL EVERY-ONE BACK INSIDE THE WOODLAND COURT-YARD.

AND REMIND THEM: MAKE SURE THE ENEMY *SEES* YOU RETREAT, AND LOOK PANICKED DOING IT.

WOW.

GOD *BLESS* YOU, SNOW. IF YOU AREN'T A GRAND LASS, THEN *NOBODY* IS.

FOR A FIRST-TIME AMATEUR, YOU *SURE* KNOW HOW TO PLAN A BATTLE.

SO, ANY OF YOU TOY SOLDIERS STILL HAVE SOME *FIGHT* IN YOU?

DO YOU IMAGINE US FRAGILE MEAT, TO BE DISCOURAGED BY A FEW SCRATCHES?

OF *COURSE* WE'RE STILL ABLE TO FIGHT.

AND WHAT'S WITH THE "TOY SOLDIER" COMMENT? WAS THAT INTENDED AS A *JIBE?*

WEYLAND! *MEDIC!*

WE NEED A *MEDIC* OUT--

LET US *THROUGH*, PLEASE!

MAKE A *HOLE!*

LET ME *GO*, JACKASS! I WANT TO SEE WHAT'S HAPPENING!

TOO BAD, PINOCCHIO. YOU'RE GOING TO STAY INSIDE HERE WHERE IT'S *SAFE*.

YOU SHOULD BE OUT THERE, TOO.

AND YET HERE I REMAIN.

COWARD.

PUNK.

DOCTOR SWINEHEART! THIS ONE'S WOUNDED *BAD!*

WHERE DO YOU WANT HIM?

WELL *THAT'S* CLEVER.

WHAT?

"SOME OF THE WOODEN SOLDIERS ARE SALVAGING BODY PARTS FROM THEIR FALLEN COMRADES TO ASSEMBLE *NEW* SOLDIERS."

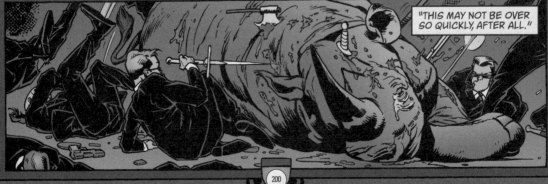

"THIS MAY NOT BE OVER SO QUICKLY, AFTER ALL."

NO! *NO!*

WHAT'S SHE *DOING?*

GET *BACK* IN HERE, YOU LITTLE *TWERP!*

SNOW DOESN'T UNDER-STAND!

THOSE CREATURES ARE LIKE ME! *MADE* LIKE ME, OUT OF HARDWOOD!

YES, THEY'LL BURN EVENTUALLY, BUT NOT QUICKLY!

AND UNTIL THEN THEY'LL STILL WALK AND KILL AND SET FIRE TO WHATEVER THEY TOUCH!

SNOW'S JUST CREATED TWO HUN-DRED MOBILE HUMAN *TORCHES!*

CALL EVERY GROUP LEADER. FIGHT THE FIRES, IF THEY CAN, BUT GET READY TO EVACUATE EVERY BUILDING ALONG BULLFINCH STREET.

BOTH SIDES!

I'M ON IT!

EXIT INTO THE BACK ALLEYS. DON'T TRY TO ESCAPE PAST THE BURNING MEN!

AND GET ME THE THIRTEENTH FLOOR!

NOW!

MAKE IT RAIN! HARD AND FAST!

BUT, MISS WHITE, YOU *CLEARLY* TOLD US TO CONCENTRATE OUR EFFORTS TOWARDS KEEPING THE MUNDYS BLIND TO--

AND *RAIN* WILL HELP KEEP THE MUNDYS INDOORS AND OUT OF OUR BUSINESS, SO DON'T *ARGUE* WITH ME!

"*OBEY* ME, WOMAN, OR YOU'LL DISCOVER JUST HOW *MUCH* SHIT I CAN UNLEASH ON FABLETOWN CITIZENS WHO PISS ME OFF!"

THE GLASS SLIPPER SHOES

BRANSTOCK TAVERN

SUCH *LANGUAGE!*

GIVE HER ALL THE RAIN SHE WANTS. YOU CAN HANDLE *THAT* MUCH WITHOUT ME.

WHERE ARE YOU GOING?

OUT TO TEACH AN IMPUDENT WOMAN A WELL-DESERVED LESSON THAT'S BEEN *TOO* LONG COMING.

OKAY, THEY'VE GOT THE HOSE ON TARGET.

TURN THE WATER ON.

FIRE HOSE

THIS IS FOR MY BOO BEAR, YOU *MONSTERS!*

YEAAUUGHH!

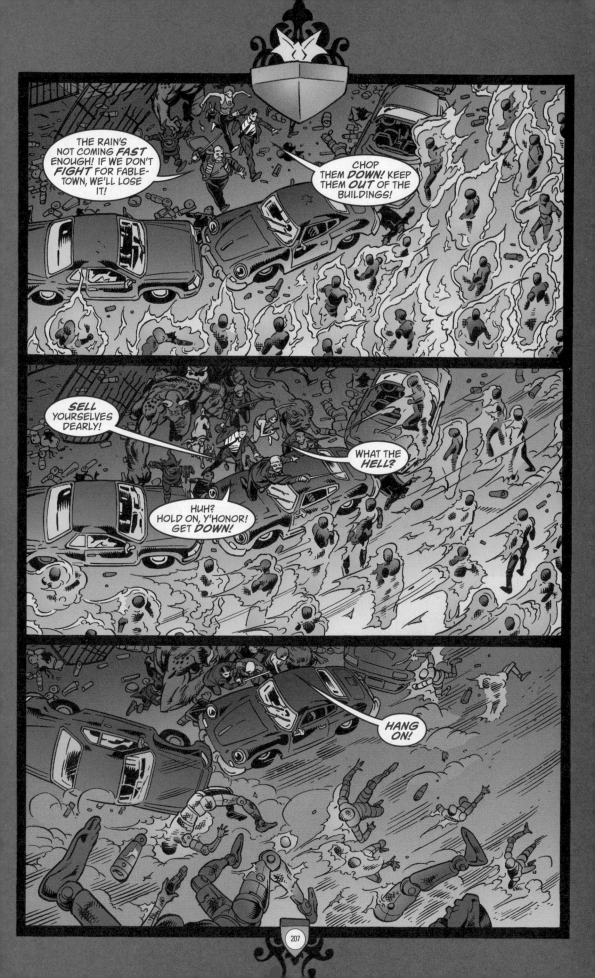

TOO MANY CANDLES ON *THIS* BIRTHDAY CAKE.

BIGBY!

SORRY I'M LATE, FOLKS.

DID I GET ANY OF YOU WITH MY HUFF AND PUFF? IT'S NOT THE *EASIEST* THING TO AIM.

MAYBE WE'D BETTER TEND TO THE *REMAINING* FIRES BEFORE ANYTHING ELSE.

NEXT: WRAPPING UP THE WAR, THE FATE OF FABLETOWN...AND JUST WHAT HAPPENED TO RED RIDING HOOD DURING ALL THIS?

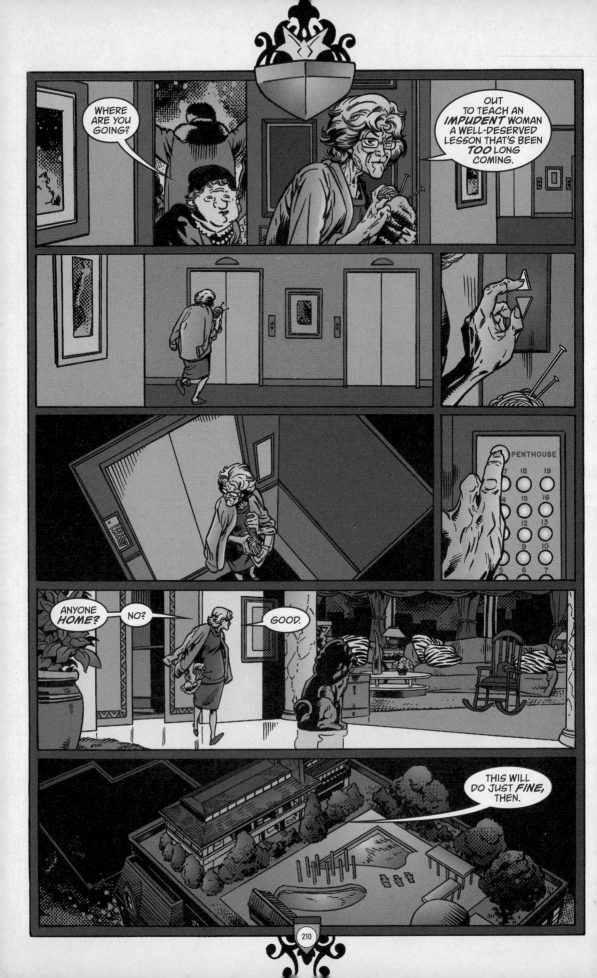

IN LIKE A LION — OUT ON THE LAM

OH, LITTLE RED RIDING HOOD.

RED, RED RIDING HOOD. UP IN THE AIR AND UP TO NO GOOD.

WHO'S THIS, PUTTING *VOICES* IN MY HEAD?

UP ON THE ROOFTOP, RED, RED RIDER IN THE SKY.

COME UP TO MEET ME. COME UP TO DIE.

WHO SPOUTS SUCH *DOGGEREL*?

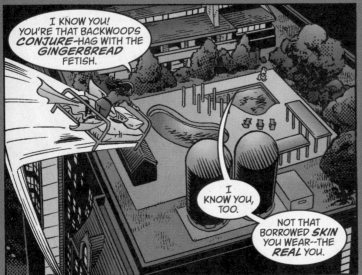

I KNOW YOU! YOU'RE THAT BACKWOODS *CONJURE*-HAG WITH THE *GINGERBREAD* FETISH.

I KNOW YOU, TOO.

NOT THAT BORROWED *SKIN* YOU WEAR--THE *REAL* YOU.

I SENSED WHO YOU WERE THE MOMENT YOU WOKE UP THAT *RIDICULOUS* CHICKEN HUT OF YOURS.

BABA YAGA.

I DIDN'T *INTEND* TO WAKE IT. I DIDN'T EVEN KNOW FOR CERTAIN THAT IT WAS HERE IN THIS LAND.

IT MUST HAVE SENSED ME ON ITS OWN.

SLOPPY WORK.

YOUR SUMMONING RHYMES WERE *INSIPID*.

NOT MY INTENTION.

I CRAFT MY MESSAGES IN PLAIN LANGUAGE, BUT SOME *BUG* IN THE SPELL I COULD NEVER CORRECT ALWAYS RECASTS THEM IN BAD VERSE.

SLOPPY WORK.

TOUCHÉ.

WHY ARE WE HERE? I HAVE A BATTLE TO ATTEND TO DOWN BELOW.

NO, YOUR FIGHT'S HERE WITH *ME*.

NONSENSE, I--

WHAT WAS *THAT*?

THEIR WONDROUS *WOLF* HAS ARRIVED TO SAVE THE DAY.

YOUR BATTLE BELOW IS *LOST* TO HIM-- WHELP OF THE NORTH WIND--JUST AS THE ONE UP HERE IS LOST TO *ME*.

AND NOW, LET'S HAVE SOME *RAIN* TO PUT OUT LINGERING FIRES.

YOU'RE SHOWING *OFF*, FRAU TOTENKINDER, IN YOUR *LAST* MINUTES OF LIFE.

YOU'D ACTUALLY *DUEL* WITH ME? YOU WERE *NEVER* IN MY LEAGUE!

PERHAPS NOT, IN THE *OLD* DAYS, IN THE OLD LANDS. BUT YOU'RE A *STRANGER* HERE, IN THIS SMALL SPOT OF EARTH, WHERE I'VE HAD *CENTURIES* TO WEAVE AND KNIT EVERY POSSIBLE SPELL OF ADVANTAGE.

YOU'VE STUMBLED INTO *MY* PLACE OF POWER, FOOLISH WOMAN.

FINE, THEN LET'S BE AT IT.

THIS ENDLESS CONVERSATION *BORES* ME.

YOU CAME!

MISS WHITE?

THE FIRST TEAM FIGHTS THE FIRES STILL BURNING IN THE BUILDINGS, WHERE THE RAINFALL CAN'T GET TO THEM.

I'LL TAKE THAT ONE. FIRE-FIGHTERS, FORM ON ME!

THE SECOND TEAM GATHERS OUR WOUNDED AND GETS THEM INSIDE.

MISS WHITE?

YOU FORGOT YOUR *CANE*, MISS WHITE.

AND THE THIRD GROUP INSPECTS THE WOODEN SOLDIERS. EXAMINE EACH ONE CAREFULLY.

MAKE SURE THEIR *HEADS* ARE REMOVED, NO MATTER HOW *DEAD* THEY MAY SEEM.

CHÂTEAU D'IF FENCING ACADEMY

WE'LL DO THAT--COLLECT THE HEADS.

STORE THEM INSIDE, IN ONE OF THE ROOMS OFF THE BUSINESS OFFICE--FAR AWAY FROM THEIR BODIES.

BIGBY!

YOU *ALWAYS* SAVE ME.

SNOW, I'M TICKLED TO SEE YOU, TOO, BUT IT'S RAINING CATS AND DOGS AND YOU'RE *PREGNANT*.

THINK OF THE CUB. GET YOURSELF INDOORS THIS *INSTANT*.

WOW! DID YOU SEE *THAT*?

FLY, TAKE SNOW BACK INSIDE.

MY SISTER IS SUDDENLY SO TOTALLY-- ANIMAL.

NOW, PEOPLE, LET'S GET BACK TO WORK. THE *BATTLE* MAY BE OVER, BUT NOT THE *FIGHT*.

WHO'D'VE EVER GUESSED?

THURSDAY, MARCH 28TH. JUST AFTER TWO IN THE MORNING.

THE LONG NIGHT WEARS ON.

DID YOU SEE THAT, FLYCATCHER?

A LIGHTNING STRIKE, BUT REAL CLOSE THIS TIME. MAYBE ON OUR OWN ROOF.

DO YOU THINK WE SHOULD CHECK IT OUT?

STAY HERE. HOLD THE ELEVATOR.

I'LL INVESTI-GATE.

CAREFUL, YOUR HONOR.

WHAT *IS* THAT?

IS SOMEONE *OUT* THERE?

OH NO..

DEAR GOD, ABOVE.

FLY!

DOWN! PUSH *DOWN!*

WE NEED TO GO DOWNSTAIRS RIGHT *NOW!*

WHAT *IS* IT, SIR? WHAT DID YOU *SEE?*

SOMETHING? I MEAN, *NOTHING!* NEVER MIND!

AND *NO ONE* GOES BACK UP THERE FOR THE REST OF THE NIGHT! THAT'S AN *ORDER!*

BUT I--I WAS ALWAYS--

I KNOW. YOU WERE IN SO *MANY* STORIES--SO FEARED AND SO WELL KNOWN.

PERSONALLY, I NEVER THOUGHT MUCH OF THAT "POPULARITY EQUALS POWER" NONSENSE.

IT'S NEVER BEEN TESTED UNDER CONTROLLED CONDITIONS.

I'VE TRIED TO STAY OUT OF THE STORIES, MYSELF. I PREFER ANONYMITY, AND MY OWN COUNSEL.

"AND IN THAT ONE STORY THEY SIMPLY *WON'T* FORGET, AT LEAST THEY NEVER KNEW MY NAME."

"COULD HAVE BEEN ANY OLD WITCH IN THE WOODS."

I WAS *ALWAYS* STRONGER THAN YOU THOUGHT. KILLED A *DOZEN* TIMES, BUT IT NEVER TOOK.

EVEN BURNED TO ASHES IN MY OWN *OVEN*, I CAME BACK, AFTER A GOOD WHILE.

HOW'S *THAT* FOR A FRAIL OLD BIDDY, EH?

NOW YOU HUSH AND LET ME FINISH MY KNITTING. TIME TO STOP STRUGGLING AND LET THE DEEP DARKNESS TAKE YOU.

YOUR STORIES ARE ALL *DONE*, BABA YAGA.

FRIDAY MARCH 29TH.

TURNING BACK TO *LOCAL* NEWS, A BLOCK PARTY ON THE UPPER WEST SIDE GOT OUT OF *HAND* YESTERDAY, RESULTING IN A *MINOR* BUILDING FIRE, WHICH WAS QUICKLY EXTINGUISHED, WITH NO INJURIES REPORTED.

AND IN *OTHER* NEWS, A FAMILY'S ROOFTOP BARBECUE COOKOUT GOT OUT OF CONTROL YESTERDAY, ON THE UPPER WEST SIDE, RESULTING IN A MINOR BUILDING FIRE, WHICH WAS QUICKLY EXTINGUISHED.

NO INJURIES WERE REPORTED.

AND IN OTHER NEWS...

LIVE AT FIVE!
CHANNEL 5

DO YOU HEAR HIM, MIKE? DO YOU HEAR WHAT YOUR REPORTER IS SAYING?

...A SCUFFLE BETWEEN TWO UPPER WEST SIDE STREET GANGS GOT OUT OF CONTROL YESTERDAY, RESULTING IN A MINOR BUILD-ING FIRE, WHICH WAS QUICKLY EXTINGUISHED.

CHANNEL 5
LIVE AT FIVE!

WHAT DO YOU WANT *NOW*, KEVIN? WE'RE IN THE MIDDLE OF THE GODDAMN *BROADCAST.* I'M *BUSY.*

YOUR ON-AIR *TWIT* JUST REPORTED THE SAME *STORY* THREE DIFFERENT TIMES--WITH DIFFERENT *DETAILS.*

NO INJURIES WERE REPORTED.

LIVE AT FIVE!
CHANNEL 5

DOESN'T THAT SEEM JUST A BIT *ODD* TO YOU? TO ANYONE?

THAT WE'D REPORT A MINOR *LOCAL* STORY? IT'S A SLOW NEWS DAY, KEVIN.

THREE STORIES, MIKE! THREE! BUT YOU DON'T EVEN REALIZE IT, DO YOU?

I'LL BET, IF YOU RUN THE TAPE BACK AND WATCH IT, YOU'LL STILL RECALL IT AS ONE SINGLE STORY.

WHAT'S YOUR ANGLE THIS TIME, KEVIN? ARE YOU GOING ALL X-FILES ON ME AGAIN?

WELL, YOU STILL AREN'T AGENT MULDER, AND THOUGH THE TRUTH MAY INDEED BE OUT THERE, WE DON'T HANDLE THE TRUTH. WE REPORT FACTS.

COMPRENDE, GOOD BUDDY?

I'M GOING TO FOLLOW UP ON THIS STORY.

WHAT STORY? IT WAS FILLER!

NEIGHBORS IN THE SAME AREA REPORTED OTHER STRANGE THINGS THAT NIGHT. MEN IN BLACK AND A FLYING--

SAUCER? IF YOU SAY "FLYING SAUCER" TO ME, KEVIN THORN, YOU ARE SO GOD-DAMN FIRED!

ACTUALLY, IT WAS A FLYING BED--WITH A BEAUTIFUL GIRL ON IT.

OUT!

WHAT ARE WE GOING TO DO, SNOW?

REBUILD. GO ON.

THESE BUILDINGS WERE CONSTRUCTED LONG AGO WHEN THINGS WERE STILL BUILT TO *LAST*. THEY LOOK BAD NOW, BUT THEY'RE SOUND.

WE'LL FIX THEM.

NOD'S BOOKS

14 FOR LAUNDROMAT ANT

AFTER WE BURY OUR DEAD?

IS IT TIME?

YEAH. WE SHOULD GO IN NOW.

WE COMMIT THE BODY OF OUR *DEAR*, FALLEN BROTHER IN ARMS, *BOO BEAR*, TO THE IMPENETRABLE *DEPTHS* OF THE WITCHING WELL.

IN HOPES THAT HE WILL FIND *NEW* LIFE, OR AT LEAST LASTING *PEACE*, WITHIN THE EMBRACE OF ITS DEPTH AND *INESCAPABLE* ENCHANTMENTS.

GOODBYE, MY BABY! MY SWEET BABY! MAMA LOVES YOU!

WHO'S NEXT?

THESE MOUSE POLICE.

THEY WERE IN THE BATTLE?

OH YES. FEW *NOTICED* THEM, BUT THEY DID THEIR PART-- FOUGHT BRAVELY AND WELL--

"--IN A VERY DANGEROUS ASSIGNMENT."

"DURING THE MAIN MELEE, ON BULLFINCH STREET, BEFORE THE FIRES, THEY FANNED OUT AMONG THE ENEMY.

"EACH TEAM SCRAMBLED UP AN INDIVIDUAL SOLDIER'S PANTS LEG...

"...PRYING LOOSE THE PINS CON- NECTING THEIR KNEE JOINTS...

"...CRIPPLING THEM AS THEY ADVANCED ON US."

OVER HALF OF THE MOUNTED POLICE WERE *CRUSHED* TO DEATH-- KILLED BY THEIR OWN SUCCESS, AS THEIR NEWLY DISABLED TARGETS FELL DOWN ON TOP OF THEM.

...COMMIT THEIR BODIES TO THE WITCHING WELL...

WHO'S **THIS**?

RIDING HOOD'S BODY.

WHAT?!

YOU'RE GOING TO PUT THAT WITCH'S CORRUPT, **FESTERING** CARCASS DOWN THERE WITH MY OWN **SON**?

AND WITH MISTER WEYLAND AND ALL THE OTHER GOOD FABLES?

WE HAVE TO. I'M SORRY BUT SHE'S TOO DANGEROUS.

THIS IS THE ONLY WAY TO ENSURE SHE CAN NEVER COME BACK TO TROUBLE US AGAIN.

DO IT, THEN-- BUT DON'T SAY NO FANCY WORDS.

NOT FOR SUCH AS **HER**.

THIS IS OUR DIRE **ENEMY**--A MOST **WRETCHED** WOMAN WHOM WE WILL NOT NAME.

IF THERE'S **ANYTHING** DOWN THERE THAT CAN CAUSE HER ETERNAL **PAIN** AND TORTURE, BE OUR **GUEST**.

ANY OF THESE BOYS *TALK* YET?

ALL THE TIME. BUT NOT ABOUT ANYTHING IMPORTANT. JUST LOTS OF CURSES AT ME AND JABBERING AT EACH OTHER, ALL AT ONCE.

THEY'RE QUIET NOW. MAYBE THEY SLEEP? IN ANY CASE THEY ALL SEEM TO DO EVERYTHING AT THE SAME TIME.

HANG IN THERE, KID. WE'LL GET *PLENTY* FROM THEM IN TIME.

WE'VE GOT NOTHING BUT TIME.

HOW'S OUR *FAUX* RIDING HOOD DOING?

SHE'S ALIVE-- SURPRISINGLY ENOUGH-- BUT POWERLESS.

I DRAIN HER MAGIC AWAY EVERY DAY. SHE'LL REMAIN HELPLESS AS LONG AS WE NEED HER.

MIGHT BE *YEARS* TO COME.

I'M PATIENT.

CAN SHE HEAR ME?

OH YES.

LISTEN UP, BABA YAGA. YOU'RE ALL *ALONE* NOW. NO ONE EVEN KNOWS YOU'RE STILL *ALIVE,* EXCEPT ME AND FRAU TOTENKINDER.

NO FOOD, NO COMFORT, NO ENTERTAINMENT AND NO COMPANY, EXCEPT US. *THAT* WILL NEVER CHANGE.

SO LET ME KNOW WHEN YOU'RE READY TO TALK--ABOUT THE ADVERSARY, OR SOMETHING ELSE.

I KNOW YOU THINK YOU'LL HOLD OUT, BUT NO ONE DOES FOR LONG.

EVENTUALLY YOU'LL TELL ME EVERYTHING.

UNTIL THEN, ENJOY YOUR STAY.

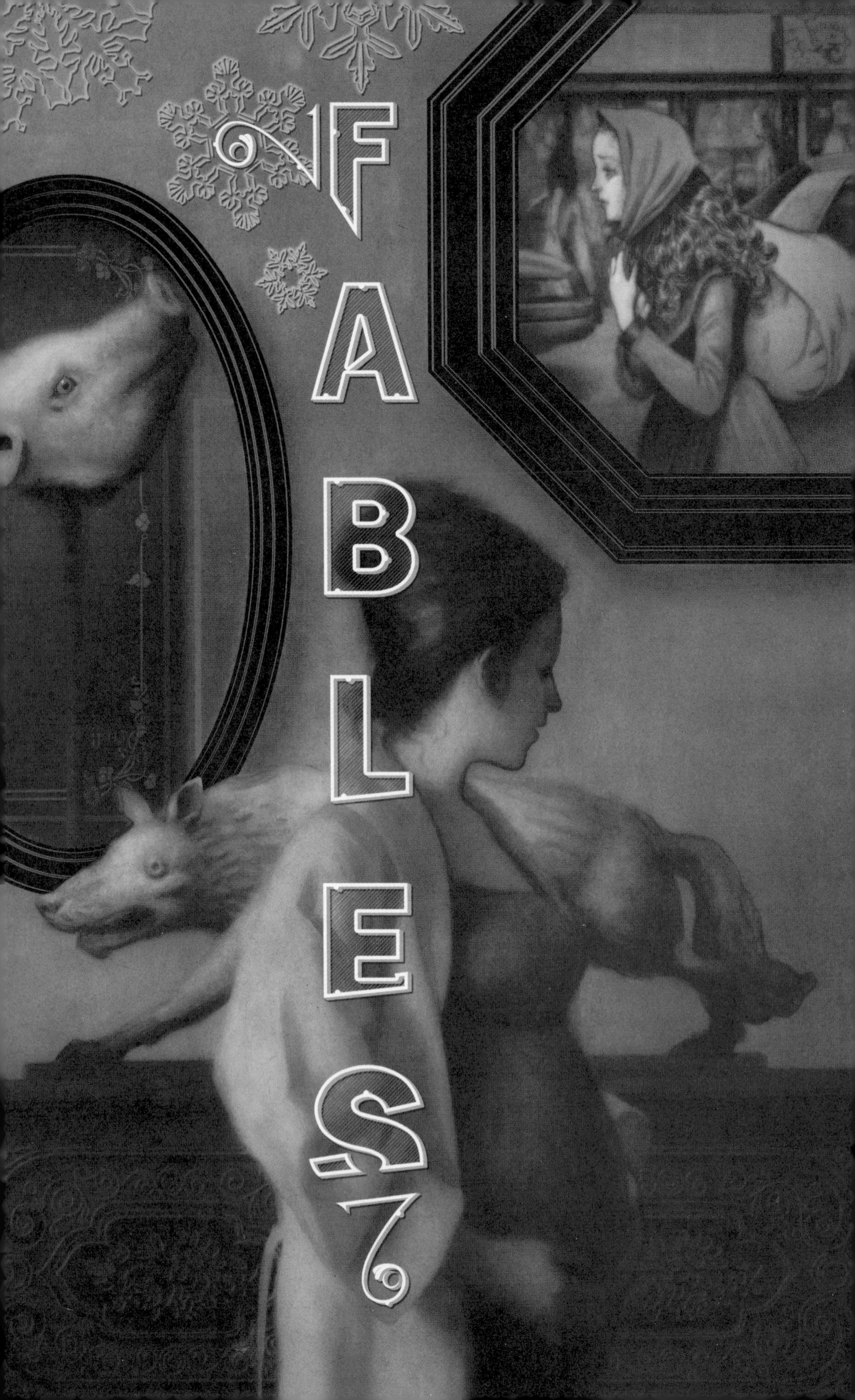
FABLES

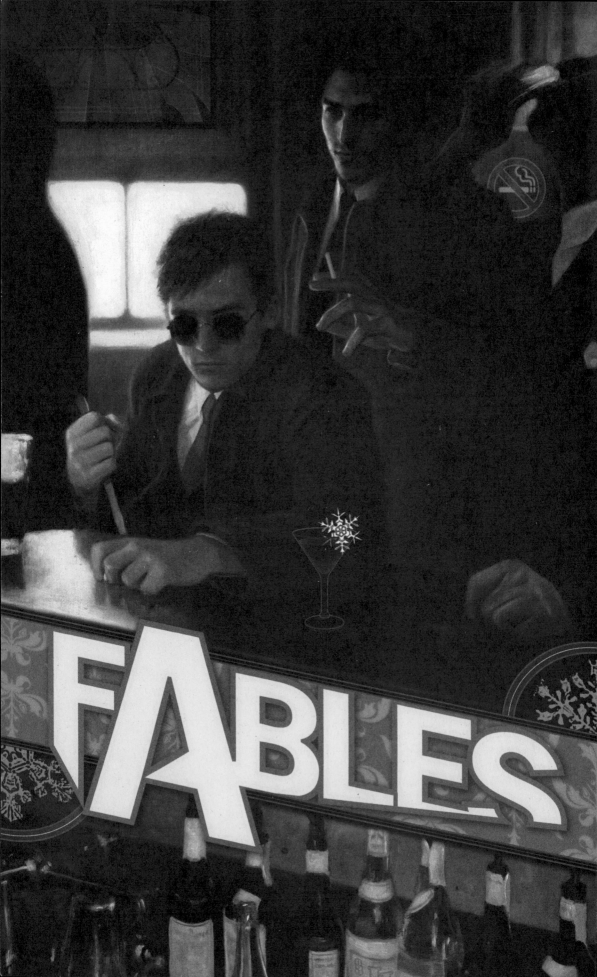

Look for these other VERTIGO books:

All Vertigo titles are Suggested for Mature Readers

Visit us at www.vertigocomics.com for more information on these and many other titles from VERTIGO and DC Comics or call 1-888-COMIC BOOK for the comics shop nearest you, or go to your local book store.

VER0014